POETRY:

A VARIED COLLECTION

POETRY:

A VARIED COLLECTION

J. H. CLEARVIEW

J.H. Clearview is the pseudonym of James Hill, the author of this poetry.

Published by E. R. Hill

A CIP catalogue record for this book is available from the British Library.

ISBN 978-1-9996913-3-2

Book layout and cover design by Clare Brayshaw

Cover image © Olha Markevych | Dreamstime.com

Prepared and printed by:

York Publishing Services Ltd
64 Hallfield Road
Layerthorpe
York YO31 7ZQ

Tel: 01904 431213

Website: www.yps-publishing.co.uk

CONTENTS

FOREWORD

This collection of poems has a variety of short poems, some analytical, some commentary, some personal and written for family and friends. J. H. Clearview liked to note the dates of personal poems, the names of those to whom they were written, and if appropriate, the occasion. These details have been left in as the author intended.

The longer poem, Cricketers, was published by E. R. Hill in 1999, and is available in pamphlet form separately from the publisher. Some minor amendments have been made to the original, including two new drawings. However, the author requested that this poem should be added to the collection of short poems, rather than added to his long poems or prose. These other works will be published separately. Cricketers is presented first in this book as it considerably longer than any other of the short poems and seems to fit the layout better.

I hope you enjoy these poems.

E. R. Hill.

ACKNOWLEDGEMENT

With thanks to Victoria Hill for her valuable advice on classifying the poems and the layout of this book.

CRICKETERS

BY

J. H. CLEARVIEW

In friendly memory of Fred Ridley, M.A.,
scholar, gentleman, Yorkshireman, and
captain of Gainsborough Britannia C.C.
for an unbeaten quarter of a century.
To E.R.Hill, B.A., a grateful thankyou
for all your skilful and intelligent assistance, Euin.

Yes, this Marton-Blyton game did indeed occur as narrated. Exactly. Except for a few minuscule, infinitesimably tiny concessions crucial to artistic verity.

Young Robert, thirty some years on, lean and fit, still wielded a solid bat, bowled a shrewd ball and took the flying catch. All the other men live on in flesh, spirit, or in memory.

This poem is for cricketers the world over. And particularly for those no longer in your first youth and who may have travelled far from your origins. For all of you, may this tale bring back to you your individual memories in the context of your life, as it does for Marton's stumper.

J. H. C. 1999.

Dave.
Anno The Blyton Game.

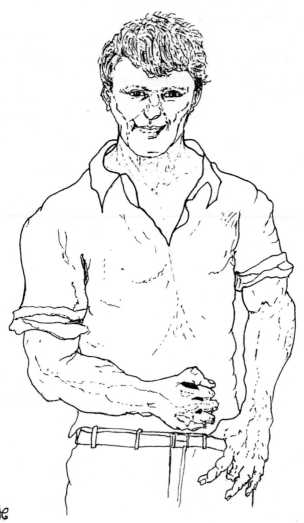

4

CRICKETERS

"Do I recall the Blyton game? Ah-ha!"
Dave's grin was as wide as his public bar.
He pulled a pint and served a double gin
As neatly as good quicker googlies spin.
"Remember Bob, the Blyton bloke, their star?
Comes in here ev'ry night. Stands where you are."
"Fine batsman, stumper, too. And Rusty Ropes!"
"Him! Ay, put paid to my half-cent'ry hopes!"
"And Lofty Light! Rod Carr, their inswing king!"
A group pushed in, the women chattering
"Them were the days! They was an' all!" said Dave.
"Yes, love? What's yours, my little passionslave?"
The women giggled, and their husbands grinned.
"Your round?! Your bloke's got you well-disciplined!"
The mirrored lights and brighthued bottles winked
As merry banter chaffed and glasses clinked.
The bar gleamed, mellow, sun caressed and gay,
While sunset shadows sketched farewell to day.
A friendly atmosphere, where one could rest
Or socialize, whichever one felt best
That Blyton game was twenty years ago.
Ah, time! – youth! – life! – how quick you come and go!

Two teams had topped the Gainsb'rough league that year.
But mighty Blyton was the team to fear!
Their fastest bowler stood all six foot eight.
He bowled such swift wild stuff as batsmen hate.
One tailender swallowed his dental plate!
At Westwood Side, he smashed a fivebar gate.
Bob Bee and Rusty Ropes were their best men.
Against those two – mm , farewell and amen
Marton, our team, we ran 'em side by side.
Our team that year – a source of village pride.

5

We won each game, though some were close indeed.
We had those qualities that winners need.
We were a team, and backed each other up.
We did so yearn to win that Champions Cup!
Those braggarts, Blyton, we would show 'em how!
At Marton, though, they near made us kowtow.
'Rain stopped play' saved us, else we would have lost.
We learned how good they were, to our pride's cost
They beat us in the Knockout Cup – we'd flu.
Against them, what could our weak scratch team do?
We both won all our league games save that one.
One match remained, the season's final one.
At Blyton. Dawn chorus in the leaves, dew
Wisped with mist, clean, sun coloured morn's fresh blue,
Life's splendour, trepidation, hopes and zest
Construed our start to end that season's quest.
A sunkissed day: rich with flowers, sensations,
Stern resolve, and hum'rous imprecations
That turned concerned as Sid our umpire fell
And broke his leg outside the Blyton 'Bell'.
Teetotal Sid. His slim son, Rob, near cried.
Young Rob, the best allrounder in our side.
Poor Sid, who knew the rule book back to front!
That Fate should wreak on him so harsh a stunt!
Who'd be our umpire now? Dave's brother, Bill.
"No, no! I won't!" said Bill. "I can't!" said Bill.
"I'm ignorant!" said Bill. "It's not my game!"
"'S easy. 'F we shout 'Howzat!!' then you proclaim
'Em out," said Dave. "But only if they are,"
George Spence, our captain spoke. "Yes! if they are!"
We chorused. "Bowled, caught, stumped, runout, I know
Them," said Bill. "That will do!" said Dave. "We'll show
You how to go!" The rooks and pigeons wheeled
About the field, and girls and children squealed
And laughed and played, each in their own blithe way.
Old men on shady benches dozed, while gay

Young yokels scoffed and posed: "You'll lose!" they yelled.
We took – and gave. The banter swayed and swelled,
As George Spence won the toss and chose to bat.
Big Lofty Light's first ball knocked poor George flat.
Big Lofty smirked – he'd show 'em who to fear.
His second ball near took off George's ear,
Then flew on through to Bob Bee, stood well back.
"Sod this!" George called. "'It's worse than 'bloody rack!
Play cricket, mate! 'S a game! – Not bloody war!"
Big Lofty scoffed: "What's 'bat and paddin' for?!"
So George smacked four off each succeeding ball,
Which made big Lofty scowl and Marton bawl
Then Blyton's inswing king, Rod Carr, came good:
His hattrick shoved our faces in the mud.
Ray Butler, George's stepson, saved us then,
Played out the next halfhour and put on ten
As 'Uncle' George stood up to Lofty Light,
To Lofty's fury and to our delight.
Three times George fell and three times he arose,
Till out to one that almost broke his nose.
Mild, inoffensive George, who loved the game.
"Just wait. I'll give yon sod some of the same!"
Said Dave. Meanwhile young Robert showed his class
And stroked that leather all about the grass.
Ray Butler went, Walt Clay, then Sycamore.
But not young Rob, who'd now scored fifty-four.
At sight of Dave stood at the crease, Light sneered.
Yon Marton youth was not a man he feared!
At six foot eight and twenty ston'?! not he!
I eat small heavyweights like him for tea!
He bowled a wide, but Bill, he made no sound:
While Blyton faces grinned all round the ground.
That thick-specced Marton umpire, what a dud!
His knowledge of the rules – well, – less than good.
Another wide, a no-ball, too, at that!
But Bill stayed silent as a sleeping cat.

The vicious kick and spin the bare patch gave
Hurled like a red hot blur at Dave.
Too late to move, Dave pulled his shoulders back
And chested down, neat as any fullback.
The thudding thwack boomed dully round the ground.
Dave, seeming unconcerned, made not a sound.
 "Aw, sorry, mate," said Lofty. "That's all right,"
Dave, casual, glanced at five rooks' passing flight.
Big Lofty scowled. Dave smiled. The struck spot stung,
But, rub it? – no! he'd rather have been hung!
The over's final ball hurled at Dave's head.
He whirled and hooked it full power overhead.
That flight of rooks should not have wheeled back round!
Its ball-struck last rook plunged towards the ground.
Long leg, Rod Carr, at full-length caught the rook,
While six to Dave went in the scorer's book.
Two overs more, Dave took all Lofty gave,
And proved Dame Fortune loves the bold and brave!
The ball hit Dave as oft as he hit it,
And when he hit that ball, that ball stayed hit!
Clean sixes ev'ry time, straight out the field.
Flinch? Nooo, not he! He'd die before he'd yield
Had Lofty stayed on, we surely would have won.
He cursed and stamped when Bob Bee took him off.
We clapped and cheered, but none of us dared scoff;
For Lofty, mad, was not a man to tease:
He'd catch and thrash you with the greatest ease.
Dave's score was forty-eight, Rob's eighty-three,
Two batsmen left, young Jack-o Scott and me.
His fifty near, Dave strove for those last two,
But Rusty Ropes then showed what he could do –
He bowled as well as internationals do:
Spin bowling at its best as seen by few
On village greens. Dave groped and poked and snicked.
Both leg and off pegs' varnish was well nicked!
But he survived. Rob hit Rod Carr for ten.
Then it was time for Rusty Ropes again.

Leg peg first ball. Dave froze – then grinned: "Well bowled."
And trudged off as our noisy cheering rolled.
Jack Scott, a duck, first ball. Then it was me.
Could I survive? Perhaps play through to tea?
Click! "HOW IS HE?!!" Not out, an inner edge.
You won't get me, you won't! I made that pledge.
Straight bat, dead bat, I met each ball. Just. Each
Strained me to where I almost couldn't reach.
Dry-mouthed, I trembled, propped upon my bat,
As Rob hit six near where their scorer sat.
A single off the next ball brought his 'ton'.
Cheer? We did! Blyton clapped. Ay. Ev'ryone.
Loose ball to leg – I swivelled round and swept.
Bob Bee fast sidestepped two vast bounds, then leapt.
Oh, what a catch! – Bill signalled I was out.

"Can't talk! I'm busy! – Double rum, and 'stout?! –
Bar help comes soon – Flash Paul and Jenny Wren.
When they start work, I'll take a breather then.
'll join you when I can," Dave filled orders fast.
"– No mate: you're drunk, that last one *was* your last.
Go home. Go on. I telled your wife you would.
Don't argue, now. You know it does no good.
Darts match o' Friday. Sober up by then.
We need your skills against them Hemswell men!
Cheers, lad. – When Bob comes in, I'll tell you when.
You'll know Bob, though, when you see Bob again!"

By teatime, they'd scored ninety-five for three,
With sixty of them stroked up by Bob Bee.
"Bill's wides and no-balls could cost us the match."
"'S your fault! – I told you I wa'n't up to scratch!
I'm ignorant! – I said! So don't blame me!"
Bill half-stood up, prepared to leave his tea.
"'S all right, Bill. Sit. Forget no-balls and wides.
You'll judge as bad – or good – for both our sides,"

Said Dave, "aye, lads?" He would, we all agreed.
Meanwhile, we'd teach him all the rules he'd need.
That village hall that sunny afternoon:
Light beams and shadows cleanly interstrewn,
White-clothed long tables laden well with food,
White figures laughing, tensed, grave-gay the mood,
Fresh flowers, fresh air through open windows, blue
Sky, bird song; ageless mystique, ever new.
Phantoms of all connected with that place
Seemed to transpire and dance about its space;
Past social states and people long since gone:
Timeless infinitude that would live on.
Big Lofty Light jibed, blithe and boisterous.
Few dared cross him, for that was dangerous.
Dave did. George Spence spoke out. But none else would:
Why risk a quarrel that could do no good?
We were a group of folk who loved a game,
Out for our pleasure – and some local fame!
We each had worries, problems, pain, or grief;
Team spirit, though, the game, gave us relief,
Brought friendship, camaraderie and joy
Which we wished to enhance, and *not* destroy.
The food was fine, the season's best by far,
Supplied off Lofty's farm down Blyton Carr.

HOW'S THAT MAN?! Out, to Bry Ford's chinaman.
Blyton: One-two-three for five. Next batsman,
Rusty Ropes. Bob Bee still there – sixty-nine.
Those two – their reputations intertwine!
Bob Bee – safe batsman of good county class.
Ropes – wild, lithe axeman on their galliass!
Slash-hewed at yorkers, bumpers, bodyline
Send it on down, my lad! that ball is mine!
A brief, mad life he lived while at that crease
As Blyton's scoreline showed a fast increase.
His eye was excellent, his timing sure.
They had to be – his judgement was so poor!

Ten minutes – forty runs went on that board.
Spectators ran no risk of growing bored!
Young Robert bowled him, knocked his wicket flat.
The next man's also. Two men left to bat.
We tried to keep the bowling off Bob Bee!
To win that match, they needed thirty-three.
They ran like stags to snatch each single run.
Their partnership soon put on twenty-one.
Then came my pers'nal glory in that match:
Stood ten yards back, I took a crucial catch.
So in came Lofty Light to join Bob Bee,
A prospect we'd been relishing since tea.
Dave's smile was grim, he paced his run-up out:
He'd either get – or knock – big Lofty out!
"No-ball!" Bill shouts. "Wide ball!" Bill shouts. Aw, God!
We groaned. All Blyton laughed. That Marton clod!
Dave uttered not a sound. He bowled again.
"No ball!" Bill yelled. "Wide ball!" Bill yelled. And then
Dave bawled: "BILL!!" "'S not my fault! It's not my game!"
Bill, agitated, cried. They'd learned his name.
"Bill! Bill!" the Blyton crowd all clapped and cheered.
Their umpire hid a smile. Big Lofty sneered.
But he part-flinched, near-cringed, from Dave's next ball
Whose bomb-like power'd have downed a dry-stone wall;
It snatched his sleeve, I fumbled, it spun on:
Bob, backing up, yelled, "Yes!" so they ran one.
A couple brought Bob Bee to ninety-eight.
Defeat seemed now to be our certain fate.
Three past square leg put Bob Bee's cent'ry up.
The cheers! – 'T was good as won – their Champions Cup.
"Wide ball!" Dave glared. "It was! So don't blame me!"
Flared Bill, upset. Big Lofty leered. Bob Bee
Smiled. Over's end. And our end, too, seemed near.
But Robert's maiden held in check our fear.
We'd still a chance to outplay Lofty Light.
Big Lofty's howl and dance were pure delight

– For us. "Aw, sorry, mate," earned Dave a scowl
Which whirled into a mad prance and wolf's howl
As, leather-glanced, by pain entranced, he danced
A Funny Bone Jig where zest's verve advanced
What ignorance withdrew. Tragi-comedy.
We loved it! But hid our thoughts. For jeopardy
Awaited all who crossed big Lofty Light.
Dave was concerned: "The bone, is it all right?"
Threats, curses, rage and contumelious spite
Depicted what awaited Dave that night.
Straight face, Dave, wordless, turned and walked away.
His next ball told much more than words could say:
Big Lofty danced afresh and cursed anew.
There was no end to all the things he'd do!
Dave, warned, their umpire went to speak to Bill.
"Yes, cut the rough stuff, Dave. He's had his fill,"
George Spence spoke low. "Still chance to win! He's ripe!
Bowl for his wicket now, and don't bowl tripe!"
Had Lofty Light connected with that ball,
They never would have found that ball at all!
Those bails, they danced, I'll stake my life on that!
They said I pounced just like a jungle cat.
Well, I had to: – Bob Bee was backing up
The prize at issue was the Champions Cup.
The Cup's fate, though, was sealed with Dave's next ball
His confident appeal surprised us all ;
It struck big Lofty's pad high up his leg,
Well out his crease, and well wide of leg peg.
Bill's hand went up without a moment's doubt,
A reflex action to the bowler's shout.
The match was over: Lofty Light was out!
Oh, passions, tumult, rage! "What's *that* about?!
When I get you, I'll punch your f....ing head!!!"
Big Lofty meant to do just what he said.
"Run, Bill!" too far away to intervene,
Dave urged, while chasing Lofty down the green.

Bob Bee zigzagged to half-trip Lofty Light,
Which gave Bill almost fifteen yards respite.
Dave stopped. "Run, Bill!" wags yelled. "No! Stand and fight!"
"It's not his game!" one mocked. That man was right.
Bill couldn't fight. His claim to fame – not that.
He lacked the skill, just as with ball and bat.
But Bill could run, and Bill was very fit.
Too fast for Lofty, not a doubt of it.
At Marton, we all knew Bill's running skill.
He'd won the Civil Service Mile had Bill.
"Here, Bill!" Dave shouts. Bill, curving round at speed,
Sped like a thoroughbred off home to feed.
"Stop there, mate!" Dave bade brawling Lofty Light.
Big lunging Lofty slung a roundhouse right
 That sleeping pill would see you through the night!
Dave ducked. "Stop, mate!" Dave didn't want to fight.
Big Lofty's onslaught matched the Eagre's tide!
Dave stepped back left, left-jabbing Lofty's side;
Dave's right hook took full force on Lofty's jaw.
The Blyton crowd looked on, amazed, in awe.
That anyone could knock out Lofty Light!
They never thought they'd live to see the sight!
"Step back, you lot – or else, come on and fight!
You want it on?! – let's do it now, tonight!"
Dave told big Lofty, groggy, on one knee.
"No, lads!" "Don't fight!" said George Spence, and Bob Bee.
Dave stopped a blow just short of Lofty's chin,
Which left no doubt which of the two would win:
Those massive muscled shoulders packed a punch,
'F they fed you breakfast, you'd no need for lunch!

"Know him? It's Marton's stumper!" said Bob Bee.
"Remember you?! I do! And 'Sixty-three!
You cheatin' Marton sods, you stole that Cup!
We should have won! and you been runners-up!"
Dave and I laughed. "So you remember still?"
"I do! That bloody useless umpire, Bill!"

We gawstered, both, that Bob had not forgot!
Why should he, though? For Dave and I had not.
We let Bob chunter, joked, and soothed him down:
Each thought of Umpire Bill, though, made him frown.
We talked of games, our lives, and way back when,
Laughed, grew wistful, pensive, then laughed again.
"So, Canada's your home for good, you say?"
"It is. From Yankeeland to Baffin Bay.
One drawback, though." "No cricket," said Dave. "Oh?
'D you like a game?" "I would. But – I don't know.
Too old." "I'll play," said Dave. "Me, too," said Bob.
"Right! Sat'day week!" said Dave. "Let's fix the job!"
"The old teams, eh? – No, 's none of 'em around."
"There's some," said Bob, " – I'll book the Blyton ground."
"Big Lofty Light!" "He's dead," said Bob. "What?! No!"
"The Big C," said Dave, "bad, rough way to go.
Wa' skin and bone, old Loft, the poor old lad.
Died hard, he did." "He did. Wa' very sad,"
Bob shook his head. "He c'me here Market Days.
He never missed. He had his own set ways."
"You were good pals," said Bob. "His dad was rough
On him when young, he was that right enough.
His mam died young of cancer, too." "He's gone!"
Said Dave. "We're here! This match, now, is it on?!"
"It's on," said Bob. "They'll want to play in this!"
Big Lofty. Dead. That's life. It truly is:
"And Rusty Ropes?" "He will! He lives down South.
He made a fortune sellin' stuff 'round Louth.
'S his multinational – Agricult Research."
"Good Lord!" "His mam still lives near Blyton Church.
Rod Carr'll play!" "Roberto, too. He played
For Lincolnshire. George Spence, too old. The Clays
Have moved. Old Ray will play. But Sycamore -.
We've problems, Bob." Time, that grim omnivore,
Gnaws changing changeless on. Men, all things, change.
We'd lives since left that early Sixties' range.

To hear them speak, and hear my own voice, too,
Recalled worlds gone in what we planned to do;
The hopes and expectations I had then;
The district's penury for working men;
The class distinctions which oppressed the poor;
The snobbery the English still endure;
The Old Boy network and Establishment
That, sneering, overrides all discontent:
It all frothed by. "Right, this we then agree:
All those who played for our teams, 'Sixty-three,
All born in either village, they can play.
If over forty." "Thirty-six, let's say."
"Oh, Bob! You're up to your old tricks, I see!
You want that man who's played this year for Lea!"
Dave laughed. Bob grinned. I felt at home again,
Transported by the mood to times back then,
The rivalry, sensations, zest and joy,
I felt them now as when I'd been a boy.
In that town bar sat some I'd known at school:
The gap since then seemed truly minuscule.
I was a part of this, would always be.
This was the country that had nurtured me.
Its ways, traditions, weaknesses and strength
Had changed the world throughout its width and length,
Created countries, shaped the course of man,
Here, much of what is best – and worst – began.
And here I was, at home where I grew up,
 Coiled in these toils round that past Champions Cup!
Dave wouldn't let Bob have his way, not he!
No Blyton pacemen brought in fresh from Lea,
Nor men who'd played for old past Blyton teams
 Some were so fast they'd split the leather's seams! –
No residents who'd flitted there since then,
Oh no! – just bona fide Blyton men!
Bob grew indignant, then waxed bitter-mad.
His mildest epithets were rather bad.

Dave, though, just laughed and chaffed and kept quite cool:
"Though you might think it, Bob, this man's no fool!
You'd try to trick us – I know you, Bob Bee!
You and your Blyton paceman there from Lea!"
"We don't need trick you Marton lot, not we!
We're still the best! – as back in 'Sixty-three!"
"We were the best! We won deservedly!
We won on skill – not bodyline , Bob Bee!
They played that long-gone season match by match,
The men, the tales, almost each stroke and catch!
And I was home again, and loving it.
I, too, recalled those games, nostalgia-lit.
My old sensations mingled with my new,
Debentures from my past long overdue,
Frustration, bondage, yearning to be free,
My life back then was still a part of me;
But life since then, my future, paid the debt:
My life was mine. The past, I'd not forget:
The good, I loved; the bad, I understood.
"– We'd beat you anyhow, you know we would!"
I yearned to meet those once familiar men,
And talk of local happenings again.
Heroes of cricket pitch and district life,
Their sons and friends – if not the loving wife!
Upton-cum-Kexby, Willingham, and Stow,
Springthorpe, Northorpe, Knaith, men from Hibaldstow
And Scotter, Laughton, Lea, and Willoughton,
And Newton, Kettlethorpe, and Laughterton,
And Gringley-on-the-Hill. All those I'd known.
"Dave, let him have his way." "All right. Don't moan,
Though, when you learn the tricks he plots to play!
Come on, Bob, let's hear what you *yearn* to say!
Look at that face, look! Look at that big grin!
Matched only by the bootsize he'll put in!"
"'Bomb' Dunderdale from Glentworth – 'Sixty-eight.
Paceman. The Kexby Curtis. 'S more! – Just wait!"

THE IRON

Epworth

Scotter

Westwoodside

Owston Ferry

Haxey

Laughton

Northorpe

West Stockwith

Glyton

Misterton

East Stockwith

Willoughton

Walkeringham

Morton

Corringham

Hemswell

Everton

dringley on the Hill

Beckingham

GAINSBORG

Springthorpe

Clayworth

Wheatley

Lea

Upton-cum-Kexby

Glentworth

Kexby

Sturton le Steeple

Knaith

Willingham

Ingham

North Leverton with Habblesthorpe

Littleborough

Marton

Stow

South Leverton

Cottam

Sturton by Stow

Scampton

Torksey

ROMAN ROAD

Fenton Laughterton

Kettlethorpe

FOSSDYKE CANAL

Saxil

THIEVES' BRIDGE

Newton

SIN CITY

ERMINE STREET

TRENT

23

CHAMPIONS CUP

·MARTON 1963·

"Aw, Christ!" Dave moaned, "I said! – just goes to show.
This Curtis – top-bat, played some years a pro."
"That black West Indian lawyer – played for Notts."
"Aw, not him, too?!" "Yes: lives with Anny Potts."
"This isn't fair, Bob, and you know it's not!
Not when you bring in all this outside lot.
This lad here wants a game for old times' sake.
You'd thrash him, then you'd burn him at the stake!"
"No bodyline nor bumpers. We'd play fair."
They longed to play, I saw it in their stare.
"Why not invite some men who play today?
Make it a seasons-past-and-present day?"
With skill and flair, they built from my request
A feast-day with myself the honoured guest:
Invites would go to ev'ry cricket club;
Details be posted up in ev'ry pub;
A buffet, bar and dance in Blyton Hall –
Dave meant to make some money from it all!
He and Bob clashed, both wished to win the game.
Dave's and my feelings, though, were much the same;
We'd meet old friends, we'd taste the past anew,
Enjoy a game: that would suffice us two.
For Bob, the past lived vivid as when new:
He longed to trounce us thieving Marton crew!
That unwon Cup shone like a Holy Grail.
At long last, now, true justice would prevail!
I listened to their details while I dreamed;
The town, the district, wasn't what it seemed:
The permanent impermanence of change
Which even non-existence could not change.
This real world. Where are two seconds past?
Nothing can last. Yet ev'rything does last.
Illusion; paradox: reality.
Part can be known, but not totality.
"We'll beat you anyway! You know we're best!"
Dave's laughed rebuttal was half-boast, half-jest

A VAST FARRAGO OF BOTH GAIN AND LOSS

The district's history and attitudes,
Variety of life, vicissitudes,
Swirled through my mind; sensations flicked and flowed.
This was my life, part of the mother lode.
Rough di'monds, gold, fine gems and worthless dross,
A vast farrago of both gain and loss.
At home afresh among my native kind,
A vibrant part of their collective mind,
Accepted totally as one of them.
This match to me would be a cherished gem.
All that had lured and banished me away
Were conquered forces of a vanished day.
I had done right to make this journey back:
The warmth I'd met would make the Arctic crack.
"We'll bring Rob's son – he's better than his dad!
And you'll remember Robert as a lad!"
I'd missed – I'd lost – so much, denied much more,
And cricket summed the essence of that score,
Epitomised the good things from my past.
This first trip back, though, would not be my last!
"Bring who you like, you Marton lot! We'll win!"
The feelings we three felt were genuine.
"Bring Robert's paceman son, we'll soon learn him!"
Had it been war, he'd torn us limb from limb!
Dave's glinting grin and wagged chin scorned Bob's claim.
Some things might change, but old Dave stayed the same!
I loved it all. I didn't care who won.
I did, but – well.. Bob yearned for justice done.
"Bring who you like! We'll beat you Marton lot!
We'll win this time, regardless who you've got!
We've longed for vengeance for that long-lost Cup!
This time we'll win, and you'll be runners-up!
We've got the bats! We've got the bowlers, too!
We'll thrash you thieving Mart'ners through and through!
Bring who you like! This time we'll win! We will!!"
"That's quite all right, then," said Dave. "We'll bring Bill."

COLLECTED SHORT POEMS

SOME PHILOSOPHY

INTEGRITY

If you do right and you condemn what's wrong,
You make sure justice can stand straight and strong.
You beat the bigot when you do what's right
By keeping truth and facts a-shining bright.
You can respect yourself, you win respect,
When you are honest, upright and correct.
When you protect wrongdoers and their ways,
You merit just the opposite of praise,
You help create a world where bad folk win,
A world of lies, injustice, and of sin.
If you do that, then you are one of them,
Become someone whom decent folk condemn.
The choice is solely yours, it's up to you.
You must yourself decide what you will do.

MADNESS, DISGUISED

(Sunday, November 10th, 1991)

When madness rears garbed in religion's guise,
Then ignorance and hurtful folly rule;
What's right's called wrong as fools sneer at the wise,
Perverting knowledge for their own misrule.
Death, torment, deprivation, all you fear,
Loom always threatening and always near:
"We know God's Truth! We know what's good for you!
Submit to us. Do as we bid you do.
If not, Divine, your punishment shall be!
And who shall judge what's right on Earth? Why, we!"
Yet who are they that you should yield to them?
They're mad. How far? Scrutinise. Analyse.
Respect the truth. Don't punish. Don't condemn.
Stay sane. And do what's right – and what is wise.

THE SPIDER AND THE FLY

(Sunday, 9/8/92)

"Come into my parlour," said the spider to the fly.
"It's the prettiest little parlour that you ever will espy.
And the way into my parlour is up the winding stair,
And I have many pretty things to show you when you're there."
"Oh, no, no, Mrs Spider," said the little fly,
"If I should mount your winding stair, I fear there I should die."
"But in my little parlour are dainty things to eat
And wisdom of the rarest sort to make your life complete."
"The dainties in your parlour are such no fly may eat
–For death's the final wisdom that makes all life complete.
Before I'll need such wisdom, I've many things to learn.
So, therefore, Mrs Spider, your offer I must spurn."
Then through the open window into the sun-kissed day
The little fly sped, zigzagging, happily away.

AGGRESSION BEYOND

(9th/10th/11th October, 1995)

Hate lunged through fear and plunged in pain, brains burst
Lust pulped primeval modern as today,
Beast human best at sanity's skewed worst,
Start first end last in madness's misplay.
Flesh splattered waste worlds in their war crushed scream,
Mashed deaths, smashed lives, with cruelty supreme:
Maimed children mute, old age numb, girls womb torn
Still, men – men? No! No! Not men – hormone borne
Cortex catastrophes, rogue vortices
Of sick purport! Yet men. Who long for peace.
Frail victims, each wrought strong, victors amerced
For their yet others' flaws. Life's D.N.A.
Insanity with sanity's dispersed.
That's why sane minds can never quit the fray.

FOR TRUTH IS

(Oct. 29ᵗʰ – Nov. 6ᵗʰ, 1995)

Each thing is its own unique universe,
However it's defined, where all is its
And it is all's, endless finite converse
Infinite in one, whatev'r truth permits.
For truth is. Concepts ghost physics' laws, hard
As reality, frail as man's outguard.
Big-Bang and evolution, facts past-packed
In diffuse now, so seemingly exact.
Each and to each seem certain but are not.
Plot cause/effect might be a random lot,
And absolutes and relatives reverse.
What's optimum at best's what best befits
Each, all, and truth. Reality's diverse
As change as truth is. For truth is. That fits.

HOME

(Sunday, October 3ʳᵈ, 1999)

"A busy month, September, a warm one this year.
And for those of us who live here,
We now can raise a cheer
– We're back once more." "Where?" "Where
We belong?" "Truly?" "Why not? Where
We belong is where we are,
And there each is a star
In one's own, a sun, indeed a universe,
A whole, a perfect
Entity however imperfect.
And with that terse
Thought, we're home again."

LIFE'S WHY

(Written Sunday, December 1st, 2002)

We don't want tears, but only smiles;
For all life's years we've known pain's wiles
That gnawed and tore, still leer and lurk.
So now a while, with solstice cheer
We'll bawl and roar with laughter's quirk
And thus beguile the fleeting year
At cold, vile, blackest. Sing, soul, bright,
Rich, lush lilts warm as love's best and hope
Of morrow's gain. Fragile is life, light
As all – at tightest, slackest; its scope
Its vessel –you. If misanthrope,
Be philanthrope a spell, and well.
You are unique. You signify.
Beguile the while, enjoy the while:
– Life's why is why.

INSIGHTS ON EMOTIONS

THE FIGHTING MAN

(An audio, video scenario)

(BAWLING BOASTER) I'm a hard case, I'm a rough case,
I'm a fighting man!
Smash their heads in?!
You bet I can!
I'll smash your pub,
And I'll smash your bars!
I'll smash your nightclub
And I'll smash your cars!
I'll kick your face in,
I'll kick your head!
I'll kick you, kick you, till you're dead!
I'm a hardcase,
I'm a rough case,
I'm a fighting man!

(RATIONALLY) Yes, he's a hardcase – a nutcase, a nogood man.
(TONE ALTERS) Such scum and vermin! Kill him! Kill him if you can!
(TOUGH GUY, WAILING) Mamma, Mamma, Mamma!

(HARD) Kick his foul face in!
Crush his skull!
It's no sin
To pay *him* back in
More than full!

(TOUGH GUY, WAILING) Mamma, Mamma, Mamma!

(MELODIOUS, RATIONAL) You poor old fellow, you poor old lad.
We didn't mean to hurt you half so bad.
Your mother was no good and your father was far worse.
They taught you how to fight and they taught you how to curse.
Poor old fellow, it's not your fault!
We all know you are worth your salt!
It is just that we don't like getting hurt,
Nor do we like being treated like dirt.

(TOUGH GUY THROUGH THICK LIPS AND BLOODY MOUTH)
Don't you insult my mother, you pig.
Dad was a big man, and I'm as big.
I'll get you bastards, see if I don't.
I won't forget this, you bet I won't.

(MELODIOUS, RATIONAL) Maybe he staggers home well drunk to bed,
Then a week later acts on what he said.
For he's a tough guy, a rough guy, a fighting man.
He'll kick your head in if he can.
Maybe they sling him in the local jail.
But he's out next morning without fail.
And here he comes, back on the job,
Bashing in the head of some poor slob,
Perhaps somebody who tried to be kind;
Whoever it is, he doesn't much mind,
So long as his victim is weaker – he'll do!
Perhaps his next victim might even be you!
For he's a hardcase, a bad case, a fighting man!
He'll kick your head in if he can!

(FIGHTING MAN GROWLS BAWLING) Fighting man! I'm a fighting man!
Kick your head?! You bet I can!

(RATIONALLY) His parents were too hard, or soft, or else spoilt him rotten,
They were loved, they were hated, or are dead and forgotten.
Everyone knows he's a menacing worry,
Wherever he goes, folk flee in a hurry.
People don't care why he is what he is.
They fear those boots and that intent of his.
So what are we to do with this social stain?
Jail him, castrate him, put a bullet through his brain?
Whatever we do, let's look at his past
And root out the facts, right down to the last.
Perhaps in that way we can devise some plan
To be finally rid of the fighting man.
Your fighting man has a damaged soul,
And he fights because he wants it whole.
He hurts and suffers for his many faults,
And that's why he wrecks bars and beats up dolts.

He's a bum, he's scum, he's all you hate.
But look well and hard – he's YOUR OWN fate.
How many lives have YOU wrecked and YOU torn?
How many innocent lashed with YOUR scorn?
How many ruined, exploited, or hurt?
How many trodden on, treated like dirt?
Perhaps one of those was that fighting man.
So now he'll kick your head in if he can.
Fighting man! Oh fighting man!

(FIGHTING MAN) Yerr! Oh yerr! I'm a fighting man!
Kick your head in?! You bet I can!
Rip your heart out, and your liver!
Yes, you bastard, you can shiver!

Think you're better than me?! You're not!
I'll fuckin' soon show you what's what!

(NARRATOR RESUMES) Ev'ry murderer, gangster and crook
– The fighting man wherever you look–
Unscrupulous careerist, business swine,
All those who grab whatever's yours and mine,
Their reasons and their causes are very much the same:
Parents, society and heredity're to blame.
It's one vast mass of problems, right enough.
But mankind can solve them, we've got the stuff!
Teach parents NOT to hit children, shout and be cruel.
Such bullying intolerance is hatred's fuel.
Teach them to be kind, to be truthful and fair,
And give children friendship BEFORE they despair.
Ensure good homes, food, clothes, and health,
Cooperation, a little wealth,
Then you're well on the way to being rid of most trouble
That destroys human lives and turns the world into rubble.

When these things are not done, we're back once again
To allowing the suffering and endless pain,
To that fighting man, hurting, showing his power
And proving he is right by making us cower.

WHORE

On the city street she stands,
With a ravaged face and soul,
On sale to all she meets,
Broken by drink and drugs,
And by working for pimping thugs.
Nobody cares if she breaks and cries,
And nobody cares if she drops and dies,
And nobody hears the long and silent screams
From that woman there
With the dyed red hair
Who once dreamed dreams.

Brighteyed as a child she played
With her toys, and friends at school.
Conflicts at home went deep:
For Father drank and swore
While dearest Mother played the whore.

No matter how the child begged and yearned,
She was ignored, till, at last, she learned

That hope of love from those two was quite in vain.
So she turned elsewhere
For someone to care
And ease her pain.

Excitement and thrills and joy,
Tenderness and ecstasy,
Understanding, warmth, peace:
All the things young girls plan,
When they're searching for a man
To share their lives and to bring delight,
Harmony, happiness, all that's right,
She felt them all, and yearned for a love so true
–For that would be hers,

Yes, it would be theirs,
That fact she knew!
Life goes the way it does go:
The strong crush and rob the weak,
The smart exploit the strong,
Lies, flatt'ry and false friends,
And selfdeceit that rarely ends.
She fell for a man; he loved her too;
Or said he did, but it was not true:
To sell sex to men would give them both their start.
"Here, please, take this pill
Then you won't feel ill,
My darling heart."

She paid all his debts in full.
He spent all she earned and more.
She learned he'd other girls.
He beat her with wild hate,
Swore his love was beyond debate.
In masochistic and fearfilled pride,
She trusted him though she knew he lied:
For he was so weak and needed only her.
And when her health went,
And the money, spent,
He left her there.

She grew well and sought him out.
He lived off her as before
Till killed in a pub-club brawl.
Drugs dull selfhate and pain
By destroying body and brain:
Abused by many and loved by none,
She's hard, and bitter at ev'ryone;

So nobody hears the long and silent screams
From that woman there
With the dyed red hair
Who once dreamed dreams.

GILLIAN

Although you shrivel many with your spite
And lash to nastiness the mindless ones,
I could not hurt you though it would be right
To change to ducklings all your lovely swans.
Your stormy ways are bred from lurking dreams
That torture thirsting you with loving streams.
Your body craves a soothing, peaceful joy,
Your mind a cleansing from dank hatred's cloy.
Spite floods the heart not confident or sure,
And weakness reigns in souls that never feel secure.
How could I hate you, hurt you, when I know
The beatings of your pure and inward mind?
How could I loathe you when I see good flow
And glimpse the tender fruit beneath the rind?

LOVE'S ENDING UNENDING
(26/27-10-1991)

One can compare you to a winter's night
With gale-flung sleet that turns to ice and snow,
A fertile land made barren by time's spite
Where none but fools and masochists dare go.
Those raging gusts that scream with trebled force,
Like you and yours show not the least remorse.
That bush-banked haven isn't what it seems –
For, clawing blind, you cloud such cat-iced streams.
The warmth-starved wanderer would surely die
If left out there beneath your bare bleak sky.
Where once was hope of all that's good and right
Is now a scope for endless pain and woe.
Past changes say you'll change anew. You might.
But not for me you won't. That much I know.

ALONE – IN MONOTONE

(3rd November, 1991)

To feel alone makes black the brightest day;
Sends sanity afar; brings madness near;
Arrays the infinite on blind display;
Perverts the best to let the worst appear.
No exit from one's suffering and pain.
All hope of help is meaningless. In vain.
No antidote can cure this pois'nous strife:
The venom is itself your very life.
So, you should die. – No! – Then you wish to live
And know the treasures life alone can give?
By doing what has made you what you are?
Change. – How? – Choose. – What? – That which is good for you,
The simple needs that none will wish to bar;
Whatever forwards health: and what is true.

PASSION

While I was fooling
Passion came ruling,
Now there's no cooling
This love of mine,
This love of mine.

For all my feeling
My thought is stealing
My mind areeling
To where you are,
To where you are.

Awareness leaping,
Even when sleeping,
Hewing and heaping
My need for you,
My need for you.

With laughter shaking,
Or torment breaking,
Giving or taking,
You're my desire,
You're my desire.

Senses cascading
Warmth never fading
Vibrantly raiding
Each part of me,
Each part of me.

Ecstasy roaring
In passion soaring
Clinging, adoring,
You are my love,
You are my love.

My burdens easing,
Gentle and pleasing,
Yet sometimes teasing,
You keep life new,
You keep life new.

Against Fate's blighting,
Mankind's indicting,
The whole world fighting,
I'd die for you!
I'd die for you!

Rows may burst flaring,
But I'll stay, sharing,
And always caring
For you, my love,
For you, my love.

Together growing,
Content bestowing,
Griefs and joys knowing,
Living as one,
Living as one.

CONVERSE

"Do not write a long poem. I do not like a long poem.
You'd write in vain, it's such a strain
For me to read a long poem."

"But one that's wise and full of wit, that's shrewd, indued
With insight's perspicacity and pulchritude,
Fit to twit fools for folly, make them think.
A well of wisdom, if you will, where fools may drink
And quench the thirst of ignorance with knowledge."

"Should fools think to drink at wisdom's brink,
Their reflection there would be but folly
– Their own, which they would love as wisdom
Or hate as wisdom but not as folly."

"Beauty, then? Beauty, diverse and sensitive, profuse and exquisite,
That proffers all that's requisite
For ev'ry taste, from chaste to rude,
For ev'ry attitude,
That plays and works the language of and through mankind
As with a mastermind,
The tale of all mankind for all mankind,
With simile and symmetry,
Metaphor, asymmetry,
Erudition unconfined,
And the truth, unrefined.
A poem of beauty,
Of pure beauty,
With beauty's pure allure,
Beauty, most refined."

"Oh, do not write a long poem. I do not like a long poem.
You'd write in vain, it's such a strain
For me to read a long poem."

"Then should I write a short poem?"

"Yes, please do write a short poem,
A short, shortshort, short poem."
"How short a shortshort, short poem?"

"Who knows?"
"This long?"
"Too long.

For I like only prose."

IN LONDON TOWN

In London town there lives a man
Who had his home in Isfahan.
Of booze and women he was fond,
So drank some whisky with his blonde.
Some mullahs chanced upon the pair;
Since booze and sex are banned out there,
They tanned his arse with fifty strokes,
Those dirty stinking Moslem blokes,
And with his blonde committed seegeh,
An act for which she was not eager.
The chastened pair left Isfahan,
And flew with S.A.S.from Teheran.
In Tooting Bec, they settled down
(Tooting Bec's part of London town).
No more he visits Isfahan.
He's had enough of all Iran.
His blonde, however, 's more than eager
To taste fresh punishment with seegeh.

DESPAIR DISSECTED

(29-31/3/1993)

Tell lies not truth! All honour to the lie!
Let scum and vermin rule the world! They do!
Oh yes, they do!!! Truthsayer? Let him die!
Nothing for him! Let him eat shit and spew!
Blind him! Tear out his tongue! Don't let him live!
But, first, steal all he has to give.

You, politicians, priests – you?! leaders??! know
What's best for us?!? The truth? – you spit on it!
Truth; lie; they're both a blind-wit passing show,
Designed by mindless life to hide death's pit.
Today's black lie's tomorrow's pure white truth,
As age to wisdom grows from folly's youth.

Truthsayer, powerless, who – what are you?!
The ice spike of indiff'rence through your heart,
Or contempt, hate, and loathing are your due:
The first, their worst, shall wholly be your part.
Until your truths can smash their lies apart,
You'll stay their compelled slave in their slave-mart.

THE OM

"I'm gay," he wept, the pretty butterfly,
The om, crude man refined, the in man odd.
"We're worldwide gay," the oms' pervasive lie.

"– Queers, pansies, fairies!" other men reply,
Rude men, crude man made unrefined by God.
"Not gay, but fay!" rude men rebut the lie.

"– Gay, fay, I'm me," growls brute man brave crag high,
Still om, gorilla strong, fierce in man odd.
"I sway *MY* way, *You*! For that, *I* kill or die."

"YOU sway YOUR way, You, that, I'll not deny,"
Crude man respects the brave, refined by God.
"MY way's MY way! For that, *I* kill or die."

Man sways all ways. Life-forms diversify.
For in forms out, as out forms in man odd,
Right bends wrong straight, and straight bends right awry.

The om are om, for all their reasons why,
As odd as God shapes man as man his God.
Each has an optimum. For that, all try.
Om's? Yours? To live. As best one can. Not die.

MAN/WOMAN

(20/21-10-96 at midnight plus six minutes)

There never was a woman
who could beat a man who was a man.
He beats her ev'ry time, and she, woman,
swallows him, and is his, and he hers,
totally – if she is total woman
and he is total man.

ELEMENTAL

7-5-97

Black ragged bitches of the air,
White needles random ev'rywhere,
Rain rope chain stitched midday midnight,
8-5 -97
Electric storm; my raw mind's plight.

Then.

26-5-97
Torn trunks chunked sunder, sap, black gushed
Canker flitched, mind womb entombed, crushed
Screamed noiseless, barren mutant mute
In agony, gnarled skew, acute.

Then.

Emotions, mem'ries, facts: what then?
All. Life. More than. All. Sewers. Gushed.
Pure water. Nitric acid. Fen
Growths. Truth, lie coated, 's never crushed.

Storm primal elements on small
Earth. Concealed. Each in itself all,
All in each.

–Then.

And, Now?
–Now is now –
… and /And/ and… then is Then.

TRUE LOVE

Every woman is made for love
And every man to be a lover.
The older he grows the less he needs –except of help–
And the more he wants –of less.
And help, well that she gives.

YOUTH
(Written 1997or '98)

Here is no bum, here are no scum!
We are the young, the youth of today!
Just give us our chance to pay our way,
To work and to learn and to live a full life,
Free, full of feeling, not riven with strife.
Time, seeming so slow, flays us so fast.
Your present mistakes could well be our last.

BLACK NIGHT OUTSIDE, WITHIN
(17.30 hours Monday, 31ˢᵗ October, 2011)

Within me, rancour and bile, all that's vile –
But coated and cloaked with, tiredness… defeat….
The lure of deceit… of a better me.
Rile –… rile –that's the style! Fight,
Then Fight!!! –smash all Death's fright,
And evil –for such is Life at richest.
I snarl a quiet, gentle smile. For it is mete
So to do. And you… and you.. and you,
Should you, too? Do. And do not rue
That you do –let all conspue
That dare –for you are where you're richest.

DEATH? –*LIFE!* –LIFE!!!

(Written Tuesday, 15 November, 2011)

In all the bitterness of life's despair,
Death's hovering, enfolding with its phantoms there
That are reality, that do not care
For you except to claw you sunder,
Crush you, smash you, haul you under
With their insidious might. ***Fight! – Fight!***
Do what is right! – your right to life
Is ***now***!–once gone, it's gone forever.
Cling to the truth! Quit?! – No!! Never!!!
Ameliorate! Drag back what's gone
And build it up anew! – You are you.
You live but once. Give life its fullest due.
It's yours! – ***unique***. Enrich it while you can.

BIRTHDAY POEMS FOR
FAMILY AND FRIENDS

MY LITTLE PONY

(For Vicky, aged seven)

I love my little pony
With his beautiful dark eyes.
I groom him well, then hug him tight;
I'm not afraid that he will bite:
He knows I sympathise.

I love my little pony
With his beautiful dark eyes.
When people are unkind to me
And cruel and hard, as they can be,
I know we're still allies.

I love my little pony
With his beautiful dark eyes.
He is so graceful, warm and strong.
He doesn't tell me I am wrong,
Nor hurt me with his lies.

I love my little pony
With his beautiful dark eyes.
We bounce and trot along our way
And pluck more pleasure from the day
Than you could realise.

I love my little pony
With his beautiful dark eyes,
Through spring's green grass and summer's flowers,
Past autumn's crops and fogdrenched hours,
In winter gales' shrill cries.

I love my little pony
With his beautiful dark eyes.
He puts up with the rain and snow.
He'd take me where I want to go
However bleak the skies.

I love my little pony
With his beautiful dark eyes.
Though all we've done and what we share
May well not be the least bit rare,
I feel it otherwise.

DAVE'S WAY

(June 7ᵗʰ – 12ᵗʰ, 1995 for David Frank Hill's birthday, June 17ᵗʰ)

Dave's cheery smile and nimble wit
Beguile the while as needs befit.
He'll reconcile the hypocrite,
The misfit, half-wit, and nitwit,
Revile the vile in virile style,
Unservile serve the puerile,
And debit credit where least fit
Yet most, for that's Dave's way.

Moonrays and rain through sun-bowed grey,
Arcane, mundane, in their display,
Life's weal and bane in full array,
The heyday, payday, and mayday
That grain and skein mankind's vain gain,
Greed, love's pain, love's hate, grief, the brain
Thrashed dreamplay asway death's causeway,
Dave's seen, felt, known it all.

MONITIONS

(21-02-1997 for Euin Robert Hill by his brother Jim, alias J. H. Clearview)

Monitions on your birthday, Sir: –
Don't kick the cat or beat the cur;
Refrain from lies and wicked deeds,
Promoting spite and psycho creeds;
Adore Almighty God above,
If Truth be God and Truth's to love;
Don't praise or excuse unfair acts,
Appraise them fairly with the facts;
Wise words and good advice are dear,
Though cheap as air in folly's ear;
Should spiteful, psycho hate chance nigh,
Refrain from wrath, regard the sky,
Don't kick the cat or beat the cur,
Let truth and facts take action there.
Monitions, Sir, on your birthday,
To wish you well in ev'ry way.

CHRISTINE'S BIRTHDAY
(Nov. 22nd, 1997)

In Owston Ferry, not long ago, a boy
Named Roy, in merry mood, would grace his hour's joy
With hopes of love, of splendour with
A lovely lass excelling ev'ry myth
Of ancient times, perfect, or nearly so
For him. He sought with care. For he'd make no
Mistake with her, his choice of mate: a girl
Who'd set his mind a-whirl, one he'd unfurl
His whole life for and share it to their full.
They met. They wed. And life was beautiful.
Though pain and care have battered at their life,
Christine for Roy has proved a worthy wife
And mother and friend. So, Christine, we're here
Today, your birthday, to honour and cheer
And encheer you as merit wills and all want.

A SWEDISH LADY'S BIRTHDAY
2/10/1998

One's birthday comes but once a year,
And when it does, Swedes raise a cheer,
Four, in fact –and sometimes more,
Sometimes they even reach a score!
Five times that score's a youthful age
For Fru Wilma Lindahl, Norrland's sage.
And when THAT score's been reached and breached,
It's time to live for twenty more!

BIRTHDAYS AND NON–BIRTHDAYS

(18. 10. 1999)

Birthdays and non-birthdays, which will you choose?
Birthdays are rare, the others, well, too.
Which will you choose? Whichever you choose
The other will lose. So you'll choose both
And lose none. A wise choice. For both
Are life, and life one must not lose but always choose
And live as well as one can: that, one must – or should – always do!
And you DO too!

A PLEASANT SCENE

(I put this verse on a post card of Carl Larsson's painting, 'Breakfast under the big birch' and sent it for Euin's birthday, 2000)

A pleasant scene for a pleasant day
–None pleasanter, Euin, your birthday.
The rain may sile, the world be vile,
But friends will smile and none revile
You, Euin, that, I dare assert.

DAVE'S BIRTHDAY, 2001

(Written Sunday, 11ᵗʰ June, 2001)

What can I say that's not been said?
Encyclopaedias many times read,
All that's lovely, all that's fine,
All that's learned, wondrous and wise,
Riches unending, banquets and wine,
Intricate, exquisite, glories divine,
The sum of sublimity wit can devise –

ONE'S AGE

(I wrote this poem on August 29ᵗʰ, 2001 for the ninetieth birthday of my father's youngest brother, Frank Hill)

One's age is an always consisting of now
As life is its answers to why and to how.
The who, what and where regarding Frank Hill
Began in the womb of Jessica Gill,
Beckingham wife of Marton's Bob Hill.
His uncle and aunt, George and Lou, raised him
For ill and for well at Fate's flick and whim.
A Hanson his wife, officer by grade,
A gifted wood sculptor by choice though not trade,
A family man whose best sometimes worst
Reversed just approval from last to first.
Occasion is what occasion is.
Frank, ninety is this occasion.
One hundred next.

MÄLARLAND

(Vällingby, October 5ᵗʰ, 2001)

Mälarland glints with a sunshine grin,
"The summer's not gone, autumn's not here.
Come out! Enjoy me! Don't stop in.
Hares nibble and lollop, birds pick and peer,
In Grimsta woods you can view roe deer.
On with the mood that lets you win!
It's here for the having – so why not begin?"
Sadness and sorrow, gloom and despair,
They always abound, they're ever there.
But a sun-kissed day with a warming smile
Can beguile them away with its life-rich wile.

TRUST ONLY TRUTH

*(For David Frank Hill on Sunday, June 9ᵗʰ, 2002. Originally titled,
'VICISSITUDE'S TREADLE, I changed it on March 7ᵗʰ, 2007
because Truth, ultimately, always comes first for me)*

Time tramping inroads, vicissitude's treadle,
Churns whims, life a-crumble, flaked dust scattered wide.
Fast fortune slowed past remorseless a-meddle
Heeds only wisdom as ruler and guide.
Trust only truth, judicious and sure.
Where all else fails, truth will endure.

FRU LINDAHL'S BIRTHDAY, 2002

(Written Sunday, 13/10/2002, before I got up)

Birthdays come but once a year
With cake and wine, smiles 'n' good cheer
For some, for most –you're one.
Birthdays come, but they're soon gone.
Non-birthdays, now –a-ha! We like them, too.
You love them when they're good to you!
And that's what we wish. For all days.
Happy birthday, Mrs Lindahl!

TIME'S HAUL

(Mrs Lindahl's birthday card, Oct.13th, 2003)

Time is easy, time is hard.
Time is all in each regard.
It holds all
In its haul.
May your all be gentle peace,
A rich soul throughout life's lease,
Flashes of joy through quiet days,
And always inner contentment raise.

HALE! LIFE'S RICHEST BEST!

(Friday, 20/2/2004 for Euin's birthday, Feb. 28th, 2004)

Hail spikes down on the Pennine Chain,
And snow drifts deep the Snake.
Bleak storms roar chunked slung moraine,
Ice jags rock, turf and brake.

But, safe, belov'd at home with friends around
Is where warm life's full, richest best is found.

STROLLING

(Dave's birthday poem, 2004, composed 10/6/2004)

Whispering wind windling the grass,
Lilting the landscape lovely today,
Rivelling the river quicksilver and brass,
Midsummer mélange, carefree, at play.

Life's serious business, fleeting and fine,
Arid as torment, fecund as divine,
One man and his dog savour it all,
The man with his mind, the dog with its all.

Mid mid-June morning they take their stroll:
Countryside finery, wholesome and whole,
Healthy for body, enriching for soul,
Pattern englorying their patrol.

When you feel it, inside you,
Beauty is simple, happiness, too.

CHOICE

(Written Tuesday, February 22nd, 2005 for Euin's birthday, February 28th)

Today I'll write a poem for you,
A simple poem, that's all I'll do,
A simple poem, that's all I can,
A simple poem from a simple man.

One does one's best, life, its worst
Where first is last, last the first,
Which is which, ill or well,
All, each, tell…
Choose…
Existence does…
You.

BIRTHDAYS

(10/6/2005 for my brother David Frank Hill's birthday)

Birthdays come, and birthdays go,
Ripples in the summer snow,
Sun glints in the winter gale,
Spring flowers in the autumn hail.

Hale and hearty, strong and slim;
Body and mind in perfect trim:
What we will, we can achieve,
Avoiding delusions that deceive.
Founding in facts, striving with skill,
Means optimum well minimum ill.

Youth is fleeting, age comes fast,
Death destroys us all at last,
But while we're here, we're here to live,
Use, or abuse, all life can give.
Choose. Life is choice. Truly. Yours.

BRETHREN IN TRUTH

(Written Thursday, 23/2/2006 for Euin's birthday, 28/2/2006)

The years come and the years go
– Outside, chill winter, snow:
Bleak winter, bleak life, riven and worn,
Bigots and bullies ravage and scorn,

Wars and mass murder, millions forlorn,
Tyranny, oppression, that must be borne
– ***But NOT*** by freeborn souls!
Not this day, nor any day by us,
For we are brethren in truth.

WHY TRY?

(Dave's 2006 birthday poem, composed 23/6/2006)

"Why try? Why?" "Because one must."
"But why try? Why?! Life is so unjust!"
"Just therefore you must."

PAULINE'S POEM

(Written Wednesday, 17 January, 2007 – birthday, 21 January)

May all today be right and bright
–If not today, at least tomorrow,
For ev'ry day's a gift well given
–True: ev'ry day can be ill-riven
With this and that, all that can blight
And spite, tumult with sorrow.
Yet, yet, life is a wonder, rich, unique,
A moment, moment, moment, each a now
And each for you, just you, a bleak abyss, a peak
Of joy, you yourself bear and share its cause and how.
For you today, today, today, is yours to fill
With good or ill. For, it shall be, *is*, as *you* will.

MY WISH FOR YOU

Euin's birthday poem 2007
(After a 10 minute doze 09.20–09.30 a.m., 22/2/07)

All that's best and all that's right
Shall be heaped high for you ev'ry night,
Ready for you each dawning day
To nourish and cherish you on your way
In every way, and on your say.
This were my wish were it in my might
To gift you thus on your birthday.

D.F. HILL AT 61

(Composed 12.6.2007 for his birthday five days later)

You're as young as you are and old as you feel
–An adage that can both wound and heal.
The mind has its riches, poverty, too,
Portions apportioned for all and you.
Each of us portions each our lot,
Others add or detract as is or not.
Wishing well's easy, doing it's hard,
Being it's better in ev'ry regard.
What's best for you is the best from you;
And from me for you, my best, too.

FOR MARJORY

(My sister-in-law's birthday poem, 10ᵗʰ Sep. 2007)

Birthdays come. They also go
– And what the ?!#!% !? have we to show!?
A cheery smile, a belly laugh,
A damn good feed, an' a drop o' wine!
– Then you'll have *no-o-O!*
Need or cause to curse and whine!
–That's a hint (Nudge, nudge)*!*

So, take it!

TRUTH WELL USED

(For Euin. Written Sunday, Feb. 24th, 2008)

Happiness, sorrows, pains, and joys
Are all life's elements and alloys.

So many poems that I could write,
Profound or sad, filled with delight:
Honesty's best – but carries its blight,
For truth is cruel, though always right.

I'll use truth well in this for you,
For well you've earned and well deserved.
May present best stay ever new,
Apt optimum grace you, unreserved.

Though life is cruel, it's also kind.
It's graced you with a bright, shrewd mind,
Domestic content most never find,
Yours to enjoy scarce confined.

The future? – that is always now.
May yours be how
You want it.

A GARDENER'S SPRING

(Ken's 81st birthday poem, written 24/3/2008)

Another spring, fresh and clear,
Gardeners ev'rywhere appear,
Digging and planting, full of good cheer,
Expecting a bumper crop this year.
And why not? If all goes right,
A bumper crop's indeed in sight!

FOR YOUR DELECTATION

(Dave's birthday poem, written June 15th, 2008)

Mid-summer days and midsummer nights,
Life's profundities ever in flight,
All that is wrong, all that is right,
Packed in each moment, delight's despairs, despair's delights,
All here for your delectation.
Ripples on the Trent, cry of the birds,
The sensual ruck of all, heedless, needless of words,
Yours –if you will, if you would,
If you can, if you could
Partake. You should. You can.
So, do so.

TIME'S TUMULT

(Pauline's birthday poem, 2009, written 13/1/2009)

Life is what you make it, with all its joy and tears,
Episodes of ecstasy, tragedy and fears,
Triumphs won and treasures lost
And new ones found, gained and tossed
Into time's tumult, transmuted as all is to now.
Your life comprises pluck and enterprise,
Harsh circumstance, adversity compelled to bow
To your will and what you judged as wise
–Not always rightly. But mostly so.

A CERTAIN DAY

(Euin's birthday greeting, 2009, composed just before midnight,
Tuesday, 24.2.2009)

To wish one well on a certain day,
Be bright and cheerful in ev'ry way,
Babble and gabble and dabble in wit
Knowing it sounds like a load of …?
I chuckle and grin at the thought of it.
A wise man said that I'm a fool.
I looked straight back and saw him drool.
"Drivel!" he said – "No!!! –that was me!
If you look hard at him you'll see him –
Ha –hah! –but you won't. He would't dare."
That missing rhyme – it wasn't a load of ….
It was a load of. It was –
"Yes! Yes?" "It was a load of – wait for it –
Are you tired? I would be if I'd been waiting
As long as you to get the point.
Oh, that's alright then!
I'll give you ten out of ten –
For your perfect *HIT!*

WHERE ARE THE YEARS THAT WENT?

(David's birthday poem, written 12.6.2009)

Where are the years that went?	Here.
Where have they been?	Here.
Where will they go?	Here.
Then?	Then.

LIFE'S FIRST CRY

(Euin's birthday poem, 2010, composed Saturday, 24/2/2010)

A day to celebrate, your day, Euin.
Not with a card, but a smile, a grin:
Early that Sat'day afternoon in 'Forty-eight,
At ten pounds plus –and not arriving late –
You popped out shouting, "Hey! It's me!"
Though it came out 'A-lah-h!'– you were too wee
To speak other than baby speak.
But you've learned how since, and to best effect.

WELL-WISHES

(Written 10-6-2010 for my brother David's birthday)

Just now, I'm not so good at writing verse,
But let me see what I can do.
I'll have to keep this rather terse
– For what I've had's much worse than 'flu.
The images, words, the freshness required
Are far, far worse than would be desired
Were I me as I used to be and hope
To be anew. But, kind words, good wishes,
Though trite and worn, are tasty dishes
When truly meant and duly sent
As now. May these stumblers, fumblers grope
Forth, etch bright my well wishes true intent
–A consummation of all that you wish for you.

BRAVE SPIRIT:

For Pauline on her birthday, 21ˢᵗ January
(Written on Monday, 17ᵗʰ January, 2011)

Worth better than the best that most can say
On this unique, special though mundane, day.
Adversity is ever nigh,
Accepted with a heavy sigh,
But *NOT* by brave spirits –they strive.
When beaten, crushed, ***they come alive!***
Life's for the living! –both it's bad and good–
Though all too often it's not what one would
Have it be –one makes it what one must.
And make it, one must! Life is *NOW! THIS DAY!*
Ready for optimum. Let's display lust
For life, sum up, drum up our best array!
Though all our woes and foes should say us 'Nay',
Our will to win shall crush that with our **"YEA–EA–EA!!!"**

BORN

(Euin, 22/2/2011)

I should write a poem for you – a poem for you is truly due: –
Your birthday is day twenty-eight
Of month number two,
A joyous day back then in 'Forty-Eight.

Self -pity is no way to go
– 'S a cul de sac with ice and snow.
Icicled pitfalls, needle sharp and huge,
Ice covered and hidden, are forbidden proffers
On birthdays, so I will not deluge
You with such coffered coffin offers.

All that is good and right and true
Is, as always, my wish for you.
But all the other is out there
With its suffering, misery and despair.
I recall them, and feel some, too,
When I send this bearing, baring their opposite for you.

LIFE'S GIVINGS

(Ken's birthday poem, 2011)

Life's giving's all taking's,
It's all there for you.
Its takings all givings
To each as is due.

A SUNNY DAY

*(For my brother David's birthday, 17.6.2011 –written Friday,
10.6.2011)*

A sunny day, a summer day,
A lovely day – and full of joy
For you were born that mid-June day,
At nine pounds plus, a lusty boy!

The world is different now. All ways.
Always. For all… To raise and raze,
Phase in, phase out, craze and appraise,
To lull and dull –and then amaze.

Life –rife with all –all –ALL.
Why? Indeed. Each deed is all.
To raze – nought is –though seeming so –
… In – san– ity's –a-glow.

Think. Here at life's brink –we're
Always there– here, Life's sere and fear
Are ever near, for Life is dear,
And (n)ever what it would appear.

A GENTLE SONG

(My sister-in-law Margery's birthday poem written Wednesday, Sep. 7th, 2011)

Round about now it's time for a song,
A gentle song, a lovely one,
That lures the listener to sing along.
A song for a lady, who needs the best,
If you please that lady you've passed the test!
When her gentle smile says, "Please go on",
Your smile will match all Heaven's smiles!
… For such a smile always beguiles.
So smile now! –smile! As wide as you can!
A smile that will please every man!
–And not just men, but women, too.
*Yea! –all living life will smile with you!

HOLIDAYS, AND THE SEASONS: GREETINGS TO FAMILY AND FRIENDS

CREDEMUS

(Good Friday, April 15th, 1996, Stockholm)

Henceforth be blithe,
Watch winter writhe
As Eastertide
Wields springtime's scythe
Through chill dark's side.
Now warm light's lithe
And freed sun's strength
Shall squeeze cold's length
Arctic short north.
Hard earth and seeds, gloomed soft with rain,
Shall soon bloom solstice loud again.
Old myths' fresh lies
Despise what's wise.
With faith and need,
Dead, reborn, rise
–Hope's fulfilled creed.
Let man surmise
What gods he will,
What is is, still,
And change, life's law.
For Earth and we hold truth to be
–As rich as Big-bang's mystery.

SMILING WHITSUN!

(To Mrs Wilma Lindahl, my octogenarian neighbour, for her little note wishing me "Glad Pingst!" on May 18th, 1997)

With thanks for kindly wishes sent,
And knowing they were truly meant,
I wend mine flutt'ring, merry-eyed,
To smile with you this Whitsuntide.

LARK SONG LONGING

(17-12-1997. For Wilma Lindahl, my elderly neighbour, sent to her with my evening newspaper)

Home to a land that's cold and dark.
Oh how I long for summer's lark
Song high in the warm sunny blue!
And so, I think, fru Lindahl, you
Do too.

INTEGRAL TIME

("Dagens Nyheter (The Daily News) will not be published tomorrow, New Year's Day, the first of January, 1998. Greetings. W. L." As thanks for fru Lindahl's information, I wrote her this poem in reply.)

An old year goes, a new one comes, but time
Is ever constant, integral part in
All and nought, each space structure's ghost-like mime,
The fabled vanished Cheshire Cat's still grin.

And grin it will come spring, and spring and laugh
And chortle well when summer's flow'ry staff
Whirls warm magic winds a-winding through blue
Skies, puffing white clouds showering beauty's grace
On Wilma Lindahl's cherished garden.

VALENTINE'S DAY

(To Mrs Wilma Lindahl after receiving her note about Valentine's Day, February 14th, 1998)

Yes, Valentine's Day is lovers' day,
Thrilled with love, passion, and joy
Or hopes thereof. The pretty way
For each romantic girl or boy
To float along on vivid dreams
Of bliss and ecstasy. No pain,
No tragedy for them. All seems
That would-be loss is will-be gain.
Ah, youth! stay fresh within the mind.
Let each new second love the next
As first until its final context.
Then all, all, will be Valentined.

MAUNDY THURSDAY (SKÄRTORSDAG, 9.4.98.)

(For my 85 year old neighbour, Fru Lindahl)

Chicks come in ev'ry shape and size,
And some are foolish, some are wise.
Black and yellow, speckled, brown,
All trust life's smile and fear its frown.
To fear the hawk, fox, all such kind,
Are facts some chicks fail to mind.
But that's a topic we'll not touch:
It carries problems – overmuch.
At least, for chicks, fowl and otherwise.
A smile, greeting, a friendly act
Encapsule and symbolise
Easter's and spring's age old contract.

EASTER SUNDAY, 1998

(For Birgitta Lindahl and her friend, Ingvar)

For Birgitta, Ingvar, an Easter greeting!
Easter, like life, is all too fleeting,
No sooner here than flashed on by,
Regarded, after, with a sigh.
But summer smiles and crooks her finger,
Bids us mutely not to linger,
Her charms and loveliness await.
The past, unlike a chalk-filled slate,
Can't be wiped clean. Yet future days,
Through present sense and sense-kept health,
May yield life's wonders in untold ways
And, perhaps, some fresh truth, the one true wealth.

SPRING, APRIL, SPRING!

This April day's a sunny day,
Winter a memory, wild life at play,
Life zest's at work for us all.
Iced hail may flay, sleet winds may spray
Yet they but chide Spring's tardy way
With Winter near gone beyond recall.

STOCKHOLM SUMMER

The lake water gleams with sunshine
And clouds float high like memories drifting dreams,
And girls in Gstrings,
Inviting sweet things,
Lie bronzed and bare breasted eating their ice-creams.

Youths run leaping, muscles rippling,
And children shout and laugh as mothers chat,
While fathers play ball,
Grandma views it all
– As old Grandad dozes under his white hat.

Good old summer, sweet old summer
–Banal, but nonetheless still apt and true–,
Renewing our joys,
No longer work's toys,
We smile and laze and, sunbathing, enjoy you.

Butterfly sailboards flit the wavelets
And everyone seeks suckling's golden days
When warmth and ease ruled,
Content and love pooled
To shape a glory Life's shrouded in a haze.

Purple crimson flashes the sunset
–A summer night whirls stillness, and birds sing.
Oh beauty! Thoughts! Soul!
Eternal truths roll:
To such delightful, rich moments let us cling.

THE FIRST OF MAY

(For Labour Day, the First of May, 1998, and for my neighbour, fru Wilma Lindahl, this 30.4.1998 bright sunny Thursday late morning, greetings from the author, J. Hill.)

'The People's Flag is deepest red.
It's shrouded oft their martyred dead,
And ere their limbs grew dead and cold
Their hearts' blood dyed its ev'ry fold.
So raise the Scarlet Banner high
Beneath whose folds we live and die!'
Labour Party people sing this song.
The tune they use is 'Tannenbaum'.
Reform and social change to right what's wrong,
Scour corruption, cleanse and cheer their home,
Their lives, the world, create a fairer life,
Those are their aims and ends, and worth support.
Maybe we don't do what we ought
In these days fraught with fear and inner strife
And all that holds us back. But if the aim is good,
The goal is right, the means humane,
Although the word is not 'must', we should
Back change for betterment and true, intrinsic gain.

ASCENSION DAY SMILES

(May 20th, 1998 Ascension Day)

Hello, Fru Lindahl.
Now summer smiles,
And our smiles
Match summer's smiles.
Tomorrow is Ascension Day.
May it bring you joy in some small way,
Or even more, or better.

MIDSUMMER'S DAY, 1998

Perhaps we won't see too much sun,
But let's hope the children will have fun
And when the day is at its end
Happy families homeward wend.
And let's hope, too, that Dad won't bend
The elbow too much knocking back the aqua vit,
So that the day will close
In glad repose
With memories most sweet.

CHILL YULETIDE

(Written, 23rd Dec. 2009)

The seasons come, the seasons go
With their glittering, flittering, turbulent flow,
Whilst humanity welters as is due,
Each knowing as little as all do.

Chill Yuletide's here this year with snow
Here in the North. Is it 'Friend'? – or 'Foe'?
Some love it. Some hate it. What about you?

Be all as may. Spring will soon follow
With all its mellowing, "March!" and yellow
Daffodils and life abundant billowing,
Blustering, bellowing, "Be-a-u-u-u-tiful Spring!"

WINTER'S CHARM

(For Fru Wilma Lindahl, my 86 year old neighbour. November 21st, 1998)

Winter is a lovely time,
With snow, sub-zero winds and white-stitched rime.
It laces dark round daylight hours,
And icy boughs are wild birds' bowers.
It has its charm, indeed it has.
Winter is the spring that was,
And as a spring that winds up tight,
It keeps life's balance swaying right.

MIDWINTER'S GARB

(Written between 18.50 and 19.02, Wed., Dec. 23rd, 1998)

Weinachten, jul, noel and yule,
Words for Christmas time.
A tale, a yarn the world winds in,
Atomic hot and Arctic cool,
A garb well garnished with love and sin
Given and forgiven,
An endless multiplicity…

TIME'S ARRAY

(A mid-winter poem written between 12.35–12.50 midday, Sunday, 5th January 1999)

Christmas Eve and Christmas Day,
New Year's Eve and New Year's Day,
Winter slips its time away,
Takes a snip at Twelfth Night,
And through her clouds, real and false,
Stars, likewise, glint steel-white bright
Pulsating time in their array,

A harsh soft sweeping spatial waltz
That glides toward Midsummer Night
With warmth and green and flowers.

NATURE'S FLOW

(March 14th, 1999, a Sunday)

A long cold winter, this century's last,
Dark with iced night, light bright with snow,
Sucking heat from land and lake and all exposed.
But soon it will be past.

Birds riot the bare branches night-time now,
For length'ning days let them know
Frost jewelled lace will soon be enclosed
In sun blue gossamer and summer white clouds' wispy wool.

Chill soil now granite hard will turn warm mull
And teem anew. Life. Spring,
With abundance! A Swedish spring
In Vällingby, this century's last,
Advancing Nature's flow
With ever-changing never-changing past.

TEMPERAMENTAL SPRING

(Spring's first day, Sunday, March 28th, 1999)

The season turns a smile,
Then frowns frost, scowls snow and sleet,
And hours later laughs sunshine warm
With blackbird-whistles, chirrups, breathing life-song
Everywhere and in everything.

Soon, soon, in the seeming shortest while,
Winter will be past fled,
Fixed in time's groaned grown growth-bed,
And heat and rain will reign as meet
And meat for change, the style
For spring, with all its fresh quick charm
That leaps life-high in storm and calm
Exultant for itself and summer soon to come!

DAFFODIL SUNSHINE

(Easter Sunday, 1999)

Daffodil sunshine winks the air.
Magpies flit, and sit, and saunter fluttering
Gaunt boughs, brown soil, bedraggled winter grass.
Seabird and fieldfare, blackbird and thrush
Add spring. Hare and deer peer and pair.
Chittering, flittering, muttering, pattering
Everywhere. Burgeons stir in mass
And insects whirr in singles, few as yet, still fresh
From winter and anew to life new changed.
And humans, hesitant, shed dark and cold times
And joy active in warm flesh,
The spiritual ritual flesh
Homage to new Spring.

WALPURGISNACHT, 30th APRIL, 1999

Bonfires blaze about the land
And little children think it grand,
Dad and Grandad polish their boots
And sons and daughters polish up and polish off
Festive ways and festal things
As socialism flaps its wings
Preparing for May Day.

SPRING IN VÄLLINGBY

(Monday, 10th May,1999)

Spring has come! Spring is here!
Buds and flowers everywhere!
A Stockholm spring with sleet and snow
–Just the stuff to make things grow.

*Best wishes, Fru Lindahl, and friendly greetings this green Monday
morning!*

TOMORROW IS ASCENSION DAY

(11th May, 1999)

Eight in the shade yet the sun shines bright.
Leaf buds green twigs and the day is light.
The sky's quite blue and the clouds quite white.
Spring, ah Spring! Life must be right!
Ascension Day tomorrow.

WHITSUN TOMORROW!

(22/5/99)

Summer's here! Never fear for winter's sere!
Burgeoning, blooming, blossoming everywhere!
Warm and mild blue skies and white cloud
And rays sunning shadows shimmering
Are our lot as we, singing
Soft thoughts through tranquil feeling
Drift with the days where content abides
For wish and will to savour.

WHIT SUNDAY

(23ʳᵈ May, 1999)

The sun will shine,
The Swedes drink wine,
All things combine
To make life fine
–We hope!

MIDSUMMER MERRINESS

(For fru Lindahl on the Midsummer Eve morning of Friday,
June 25ᵗʰ, 1999)

Midsummer merriness, mild and gay,
Dances and glides throughout the day.
Chaplets of flowers, bouquets of joy
Gladden the childhood of small girl and boy
As round the raised pole they join hands and sing
Renewing the centuries' midsummer ring.

Light is the day and light is the night,
Light as the summer's perfumes in flight.
May kindness rejoice and happiness reign
Transmuting and banishing worries and pain,
At least for a while as blithe summer smiles
As mankind relaxes and Nature beguiles.

A SEPTEMBER THOUGHT

(For Fru Lindahl, 8/9/1999)

Back to the normal run of things,
Losing on roundabouts, winning on swings.
Were I an eagle with golden wings
Or pure thought cleansing impure things
And putting wrong right as time rings
Alarms – but I'm not. I'm only me.

NOVEMBER…
(4.11.1999)

Leaves scud and skip, crisp and brown,
Golden and scarlet, bumbling the town,
Fumbling the thickets, gauntness and light,
Dark-edged whispers, scarce heard aright,
November leaves.

Cool blue and tawdry straw wedge wayside woods,
Latticed trunk russet and gaunt bough black, rock chunked with boulder
greys,
Pooled with dew and dank, sludge mired by siled down dried floods
From last month's storms and gossamered by their haze.
November.

And birds sing still. So still. Still, it's November.
So what can one expect? A quiet life, in November.
Or maybe just the opposite and everything in between, or all around. In
November.

FOR PAULINE AND HER FAMILY
(7.12.99)

Just a card to say, 'Hello',
–A cheap-jack trick to save some dough?
Well, each expense swells the flow
And gives Yuletide its kick and go.
Cash piles and bellies groan and grow
While Robin hunts sovereigns in the snow
(Yours is his town –as you well know).
The rich foreclose, the poor forgo
While Robin hunts sovereigns, nose aglow.
Today, it's hard to tell friend from foe,
But then, was that not ever so?

Feed on turkey – yet gorge on crow!
That's enough to make Cock Tony crow
And blare a cheer this year for no
More war in Ireland. We'll cheer too.
Yes? No is forbidden. It's Yule again!

FOR NIGH AND NEAR

(For Owe and Britt-Marie Jäder, Dec. 23rd, 1999)

When winter comes, it bites and blows,
Puffing to purple poor Owe's (Oo-veh's) nose.
Britt-Marie's fair cheeks glow pink and rose
At guardian Lord enjoying the snow's
Dance and sheen as, white chunks dropping and plopping close
And about, spruce and pine, perennial foes
Compete. In beauty. And Britt-Marie smiles,
And Owe, too, Christmas is nigh, loved ones near,
The nimble moment jinks and beguiles.
Yuletide, tranquil and rich Yuletide, Yuletide is here.

TIME'S CHILL-FIRE BREW

(December 23rd, 1999)

Vällingby Christmas, Nineteen ninety-nine,
A year for celebrations, perhaps a little wine;
Men hack a breath and reckon,
And women note it too:
The New Year's begun to beckon
Now to down drown Time's chill-fire brew.

MILLENNIUM

(Dec. 31st, 1999, Vällingby)

Still white and calm yet roughly chill
The year's last day's sky sheens bright light grey.
No birds about, no chirp and shout, the quill
Of time etches eternity, not away
But now.

Yesterdays are where's a ware
We are aware we pose,
And shall forever we suppose.
We are what we were. And where is were?
On that we, some, sometimes muse.
Just now.

The world's a party, all awhirl this day
With food and fireworks and fizz.
A millennium ends, smile, be gay. Let be, try flee the quiz
Of life today – for humanity, or most of it, 's at play.
Right now.

EASTERTIDE UNTIED

(22.4.2000)

Eastertide untied by Spring,
Strings of sun and streams of sound
Tussle tranquilly all around.

Green and yellow and white and blue
Birds of every size and hue
Nest and attest our Spring.

Our Stockholm spring in Vällingby,
Where civilised folk abound
– **Plus a few others**.

CHRISTMAS

(23.12.2000)

The climate warms –no winter storms
Nor snow.
Fool-man performs –so species
After species go
For ever.
But Christmas? Never!
(at least, not yet)

CHRISTMAS VERSE FOR –

(Written a couple of days before Christmas, 2000 A.D.)

I'm writing verse this Christmas,
So why not some for you?
And if you do not like it,
Then you know what you can do!
–Better. Or even worse.
Perhaps in verse,
Chaste/Chased up and down with valid spirit.

WINTER'S SPRING

(For David Austin and family.13/4/01)

Ice and snow both come and go
While winter's spring is wound up.
Spring will spring to fast from slow
And churn, rich-hued, the ground up.

Nimble and neat with pacy feet,
Athlete, aesthete, the debonair and deadbeat,
Will quicken and thrive and zing-g-g alive!
And birds above will sing their love thus, *"Tweet-tweet."*

CHRISTMAS!

(2001 Christmas verse for Euin and family)

'Christmas comes but once a year!'
Trite phrase? But, without a sneer,
Most spend, feast and say, "Hear, Hear!"
Some drink to absent friends.
Some for. Some far away. Some near
Who shouldn't be.
Christmas is a time that lends
Itself to what we want to fill it with:
Leisure, pleasure, sadness, madness,
What you will. Where'er you be,
Where'er you flee, it's there,
It's here, and soon gone. So, herewith
And forthwith, well beforehand,
Thus I mark it, "Greetings."

YULE SOLSTICE FEASTS

(Written Saturday morning, December 21ˢᵗ, 2002)

Winters come and winters go,
Some stay green and some bring snow.
Here in the North, all are cold;
Yet if the brain, the mind –I make so bold
–Glows warm, Spring and Summer flourish there,
Though all around be bleak and bare.
Yule solstice feasts with cheer and fare
Blaze forth that inner glow:
"Chill dark –out! Go! Know and know

Well, here you shall not reign! Spring's life
And Summer's wealth rule ripe and rife
As ever where'er we are, or shall be!"

WINTER LOVELINESS

(Written 13.50 – 14.01 hours, 17/12/2003)

Petals of snow magic the air
Flittering fantasies out-fairing fair,
But nothing and none is so graceful and rare
As that ethereal loveliness entitied there.

Ah! But is that last line the final line?
Perhaps you'd like to add a name? Your own? And then?
Or, for better and/or worse,
Another verse?

LIFE'S (T)HERE FOR YOU

(D.F. Hill's Christmas verse, 9.12.2003)

Merry are the days when your mind feels right,
Though your world runs awry, all your cash takes flight,
Still you'll smile 'cause your life seems right.
Reverse those concepts, their reverse holds true,
For life's what it is and it's (t)here for you.
You are what you are and whatever you do.

WONDERING WINTER'S WANDERING

(Written at gone midnight, 26ᵗʰ November, 2004)

Winter leaves and winter snow
Mingle in the twilight glow.
The years come, the years go,
Where from, where to, we don't know.
We live them. And what they show, they show.

Life is all. Life is now.
We live it, knowing that we know.
What do we know? Only, time is, and life must go.
Why? Because it does. How? That, we, ourselves, show.
Why? Why? That, we cannot ever, not ever forego.
But live, that we can and do, as best we may.
And that is our why, that is our how,
As winter leaves and winter snow
May flow and sow tomorrow.

Though much is foul, all Hell may growl,
Truth fights with might for right.

And right tonight is all that's bright
To shine dark gloom away.

SOLSTICE

(Written December 5th, 2004)

The winds howl, the skies scowl,
Chill bites the wintry night,
Gifts and goods and good and light
Design and line this day,

Your solstice day! where joy reigns
And life's weal's on display
And all partake and none disdains
To enjoy their best today.

YULE CARD DIVERSE

(For Dave, Saturday, December 3rd, 2005)

Bleak and barren, chill and drear
Suffering shivers far and near,
Despair, death's fear, rend and grind.
Agony is a state of mind.

Elements, molecules, they don't feel,
Sub-atom particles whirl and reel,
Galaxies, countless, shiver and smash
Black hole compacted as they crash.

Christmas comes but once a year
With cards from far and some from near,
And some from some you thought were dead,
And some from some who shared your bed.

Love and affection, tranquil and true,
These I wish for – so do you.
But will they come? Probably not.
Yet, yet, they *ARE* part of our human lot.

Possible's possible, probable, too,
Happiness real, for all – and you.
Here's wishing you, Dave, a big fat chunk!

(EITHER)
Stay of the booze, live like a monk..?
(OR)
Stay off the booze, then you'll not get drunk!

Mo-o-an??? – Smile! – GRIN!!!

(Euin and family's Yule verse, 4.12.2005)

The wind may moan, but not we –we smile.
The children home, fully grown, we smile.
Tall and handsome, straight and fair,
Endowed with brains, a healthy pair,
We smile.

And they do, too, for you,
And at each other –though
There, they split a grin.
As I likewise,
Happy that you are.

CHRISTMAS BELLS

(For my brother Ken, and also for my brother Norman's widow, Madge) 11.12.2006.

When church bells ring and pigeons fly
About the tower, mid-winter sky,
We think of now and yesteryear,
Of kin and friends afar and near
And wish them well.

WINTER GREEN, WINTER BARE

(Wednesday, Dec. 12th, 2007)

Winter green, winter bare,
Winter sombre ev'rywhere.
But in the mind, ah! –there we find
All that pleases all mankind.

A neighbour interrupted here
– So this is where I'll stop, m'dear.

A STOCKHOLM NEW YEAR'S POEM

(Written Friday, 26th December, 2008 for Birgitta Lindahl –whose mother died, then a year or so later, Birgitta's cohab)

The years come, the years go,
All with frost, ice, and snow
Bringing sadness, gladness, joy and woe,
And, hope, at best we hope of best's fulfilment.

So may it be for you and me…
But that we first must live to see
With health, life's wealth, and life's epitome
In condign, individual abridgement.

CHILL YULETIDE

(Written, 23rd Dec. 2009)

The seasons come, the seasons go
With their glittering, flittering, turbulent flow,
Whilst humanity welters as is due,
Each knowing as little as all do.

Chill Yuletide's here this year with snow
Here in the North. Is it 'Friend'? – or 'Foe'?
Some love it. Some hate it. What about you?

Be all as may. Spring will soon follow
With all its mellowing, "March!" and yellow
Daffodils and life abundant billowing,
Blustering, bellowing, "Be-a-u-u-tiful Spring!"

YULETIDE PLUS MINUS

(1.34 p.m.–14.28 p.m. Tuesday, 14 December, 2010)

Christmas comes but once a year,
Greeted by some with curse and sneer,
Others with sadness, and many a tear
For all those dead they held –still hold– most dear.

Humanity, insanity… and fear…
So near and ever ready to appear…
– But Yuletide is a time of cheer!
– For friends and loved ones far and near!
So we'll be glad and we'll all say,
"We'll leave that other for another day!"

EMOTION'S NEED

(Written Monday, 12th December, 2011)

Christmas with its joy and tears,
Sadness, gladness, joy and fears –
… And memories… How, and why… Indeed.
Christmas… Packed with emotion's need.
A sigh is apt. Indeed. – Plus all other.
Let tranquillity prevail, and friendliness smile,
Thus all will beguile the passing while
And enjoy the present season.

LONELY CHRISTMAS

(Begun 17.38 hrs, 24/12/2011. Finished about 18.42 hrs)

Christmas time's the loneliest time for lonely souls
With none to turn to, cherish them or care.
It's then they know, discern, then feel, perhaps the bitterest despair.
If it enfolds them, enmoulds them, enrols
Them for a death doom, where can they go,
What can they do, how resist or flee?
None knows till one is there.
Some linger on – and on – and on … Some die.
Why? Each individual knows his or her own why
That can and does come in its own
Bad, good, or indifferent time.
Let it. Live, meanwhile.
Live. You're here to live. So live.
Let dying be. That's not for me
Just yet. Whene'er it be, so let it be
Not yet.

THANKYOU

(For Birgitta Lindahl, 8.26 p.m. 25/12/2011)

Thank you for your Greetings Card –
'T was a friendly thing to do.
Unfortunately, I don't have one for you.
Perhaps you won't take this too hard,
If I send this verse in one's lieu.
The melody may limp a bit –
But it's the best that I can do.
This greeting is a friendly one. May it hit
With your accord. It's the best my wit
Can do offhand, so please don't judge it hard.

BIRGITTA LINDAHL'S 2012 NEW YEAR'S VERSE

(Written 14.02 p.m. – 14.20-ish, 27 December, 2011)

I usually write you a little verse –
Something not too long –rather terse,
And to the point, when your greetings card
Drops through my door.
Something soft, something mild,
Something gentle –not too wild! –
No more than is required.
–And what's desired? – Friendliest greetings!
And many meetings
With folk you like,
And situations congenial –
And all that's good for you!
May these come as your rightful due
This coming year!

A HAPPY NEW YEAR,BIRGITTA LINDAHL!

(January 1ˢᵗ, 2012)

A Happy New Year,
Just for you!
May it be the first
Of quite a few!

Tranquillity,
And Peace of Mind,
May these, in abundance,
Be what you find.

A PERSONAL TOUCH

MRS LINDAHL

(For you, Mrs Lindahl: Monday, November 23rd, 1998)

My neighbour, Mrs Lindahl, from the forests in the north,
The fiery, dour and crimson will their pine-spruce-green blossoms forth
Flows rich and strong through each day's need
In her. Clean and sparse, conserving strength,
Judging each deed at careful length,
For facts and common-sense precede,
Dictate, her way, she does what's sound.

And flowers are her melody, fresh air and sun,
And exercise as is and due,
And interest in life around as one
Who loves not just the old but what is new
And vital and worth consideration.
My neighbour, Mrs Lindahl, from the forests in the north,
Who does her best each day with the freshness it brings forth.

THE DAY'S NAME IS JAMES

(Sunday, 25th July, 1999. Thanks for your greeting, fru Lindahl!)

Today's my Name's Day so you say,
The twenty-fifth day of month number seven,
White fluffy clouds in a blue, blue heaven,
If fancy will as fancy may,
Spell 'James' in the sky this sunny day,
I'll try to be worthy of these breezy hours
And smile in pace with the tossing bright flowers
As they laugh and wave at the sun on high
And as they do, so shall I
Right now. Done!

LIFE'S SMALL MISTAKES AND MISSES

(8.40 a.m. 20/11/1999. On my newspaper not being delivered and my requesting the loan of fru Lindahl's)

Life's small mistakes and misses
Occasion groans and hisses,
But give a chance for better things
When hope aspires and reason sings.

GOOD ETIQUETTE

(Saturday, February 19th, 2000.
Best wishes for your kind deed of yesterday Mrs Lindahl!)

Perhaps this poem's not worth a lot.
But then again, it's all I've got
To say that I forgot
To thank you for your D.N. yesterday.
Good etiquette and wish to please
Enable me to write with ease
This little poem to partly pay.

LATE NEWS

(March 2nd, 2000)

Yesterday's news, a little late;
Some facts and ideas never date:
Yet, in their content is discontent,
Mine, at making you wait.

I'm growing old, sometimes I miss
Through pressure around and stress and strain
And tiredness. So when I am as now remiss,
Let that explain,
Though not excuse, my miss.

BLOOM TIME

(Thursday, 12th April, 2001)

'Easter lilies', their Swedish name,
Daffodils, their English.
Their yellow elegance is the same
As is their season's wish.

Their time is swift but sweet:
"Spring! Spring!" it bells. "Well met anew!"
Beauty greets life burgeoning.
How meet it is, replete
It is, seed-ripe and rife,
Awaiting rain and sun.

THANKS FOR THE 'NEWS'!

(September 1st, 2001)

Thanks for the 'News' (The Daily News)
The bright sun's up and the dull crown's down,
The one brings cheers, the other boos.
Thanks again for 'The Daily News',
Fru Lindahl! Today we'll smile and never frown,
Though the crown's stopped floating and started to drown!
Still, it will choke back up again – some day. Perhaps.

APACHE (EMMA'S SONG)*

(Composed 27/2/2003)

You have that style, virile, so stark and male,
A man of men, a man for me, she-male
Who's learned, when spurned, love's earned with strength and wiles
In woman's ways. I've all you need, in smiles
And tears for passion's pain to disappear
In love's deep ecstasy and stratosphere.

I'll heal your fears, your tears, in safe release,
I'll wrap you round. We'll share, we two, life's lease.
Through turmoil, tumult, strife, life's shocks and hurt
We'll live our love. I never shall desert
You, for you are my man, my man! And where
You're strong, I weak, you weak I strong, we'll share.

So vile when you revile, yet you beguile
Me even then. Men! Men! I hate you while
I love you when you hurt me as you do!
When pain's your price we sacrifice for you!
Yet, without you, life's agony is worse.
Life's ecstasy is love, and love its curse.
…………………..
You have that style, virile, so stark and male,
A man of men, a man for me, she-male…

LIL

(2ⁿᵈ Sept. 2003)

Oh don't will ill to Lil.
Ill-will distils ill-will.
And Lil will chill your ill ill-will
If you do ill to Lil!

BOGGLE? –IN NULLITY'S CLUTCH?!?

(For Pauline, Norman and family, December 4th, 2005)

It's easy to moan a gloomy strophe
With quibbles and quiddits and such.
But castigate me for a trumpery oaf
Should I boggle in nullity's clutch!

Be cheerful, be gay, on every day
And not just the ones others pick!
Jump, click your heels, and shout "Hurray!"
To Heaven with the world if it's sick.
A laugh and a joke is a haven of cure
Ever open world over for rich and for poor.*

DOODLINGS OF A TIRED BRAIN

(26/12/2005 15.29 hours G.M.T.)

Seasons come, seasons go…
Winter with its ice and snow…
Afflictions, hopes and dreams
Mingle and clash and meld…
And all is what it seems
– Or not. We live – till felled
By time, and fill our days
With fell and foul and fine
And in between and all about.
And all we raise and raze are rays.

A tired man's rambling poem of little
purpose or intent, shaped
shapeless weak, meandering maunder,
Brittle as a cancerous cough, a voiceless shout
Of pain, a mindless mine of mine.

GROSS NECESSSITY

(June13th, 2006)

Light and bright and all delight,
Hurtless adventure, all good and right,
Don't grace your ev'ry day and night;
But sound bowels will, and a healthy *–sh-h*….

Light and bright and all delight,
Hurtless adventure, all good and right,
May all be yours, good health your plight.
Wealth? Well… what richer wealth than a good sound *–sh-h*….

For special days, a special delight,
Hurtless adventure, all good and right,
May a chunk be yours, each day, each night
– Not forgetting your daily *sh-h…!*

WHILE WAITING FOR A TRAVEL AGENT

(Written Friday, November 9th, 2006)

Stockholm, bleak and bare, blares bold,
Grimly grinning at young and old.
Friday night! Ah! – ha, ha! Gaiety reigns.
Tonight we forget week work-a-day pains!
Love will be ours, laughter and glee!
Tonight I'll meet the man for ME!
Handsome and witty, bold, debonair,
A gentleman yet a bold corsair!
Who'll give his all, his life for me.
Tonight I'll meet him – just you see!
Sometimes it happens just that way.
Indeed, it happens ev'ry day!
So why not tonight, just for me?
And when we meet – *then* we'll see!

WARRIORS!

(Written May 7th, 2007. A battle song to the tune 'Garryowen'.)

"We're armed, well trained and full of might.
We've honed our skills in many a fight,
We're fighting for our lives and right.
To us shall be the glory.

"We're here to win and win we will.
You, we'll maul, and you we'll kill!
Of slaughter we shall have our fill,
And come unhurt through all this!"

"The talking's done, the fighting's near,
We are the ones you have to fear.
So shake and shiver, we are here!
Your death shall be most gory!

"So, fling down your arms 'n' run away!
Find some safe place to hide and pray!
That is the way to earn your pay!
–And when we come –surrender!"

"For if you venture battle hard,
Your blood shall blotch our slaughter yard!
While we'll come through unscathed, unscarred,
And then go on a bender!"

"And when peace comes, all fighting done,
Then home we'll go to quieter fun,
Old friends, and love renewed, new won
With passion's glorious bliss!"

LITTLE VICKY

(Written 5.6.2008)

Little Vicky, fresh and rare,
Arms and legs waving the air,
Laughing and chuckling,
Happiness haloed in her blonde hair.

Toddling, exploring, learning her world,
Life's baby mysteries swiftly unfurled.
Sweetness and light, her mother's delight,
And for Vicky's dad her simply being kept things right.

LIFE'S RIDE

(Written 9/12/2008)

We don't want grief, we abominate pain.
–Loss? No, thanks! Just benevolent gain
Will tickle our taste and make us grin.
Let life be lovely, suit our taste.
When we venture, please let us win!
Good fortune, stay long, bad –depart in haste!
Life is unique –for use… and abuse.
Chance, seeming random, may not be so loose.
We choose each moment though it choose us
–Remember that well when you start to cuss!
In the ride of life you drive your own bus.

ENOUGH!

(Wed. 10/12/2008, 14.30 hours)

Enough of this stuff –woes and strife!
We're here to live – we've only one life.

THE YEARS THAT FLED

(March 14th, 2011)

Where are the years that fled?
They're part of those to come.

Happy is the man who has a home
Where cherished loved ones live.
Such a man need seldom roam,
For he has the best that life can give.

THE ENGLISHMAN AND HIS LADY

(Written 24.2.2009 – and discovered, yet not copied,
reworked till now, 5.2.2012)

Snowbound England stuffed her craw,
Rubbed her nose chilled red and raw
    –But you weren't there, you lucky pair!
In the Antipodes bathing bare,
Shocking the natives (an event most rare)
–The few who saw.

Back from your travels, bronzed and glad,
Back to the humdrum, drab, dear drear,
England's daily riches, where little's to fear
And much superb – yet with bits bad…
Two British patriots, happy and gay,
Whistling and singing the blithe, long day!?
Is that true?? –Or would you rather not say?

A SENTENCE

A sentence is like being sentenced a walk,
Where a comma's your judgement to pause, and gawk;
After walking and gawking, you may want to sit,
And semi-colons will let you where places permit;
Since semi means partly, your journey's not done;
But your next stop is dinner, by this colon:
Full sentence digested, with one final hop,
You finish it off at its full stop.

CROSS TALK

(12.15a.m Saturday, December 3rd, 2011)

All the uttermost of despair
Splatters its bitterest in the air.
–What air? All. The mood is such. –Doubt –fear.
Poet? –? – Are you? Yes. Are you? *A-a-re* you?
Yes. A mediocre nobody's poet that's what you are.
– For critics who lack in judgement.

EXISTENCE

(Composed 10/6/2003)

As lovely as life in perpetual bloom,
As ugly as folly dispensing its doom,
As soft-hard as ignorance, vile-sweet as deceit,
Discreet as discretion, discrete as afreet
… Existence holds all.

For each its decisions, to each its way:
Whatever the choice, each itself shall pay.
What is *your* choice? – That, only you can say:
For you make your choice ev'ry moment each day,
Whether wise or foolish, events assay.
… Existence holds all.
Yours is now. Use it well. If not, it will use you.

The strongest is weak and the weakest strong
When truth's guiding might in righting what's wrong.

* * *

THE GIFT OF BLACK ISLE
Highland Healers, Book 5

Published by Keira Montclair
Copyright © 2022 by Keira Montclair

This is a work of fiction. Names, characters, places and incidents are either the product of the author's imagination or are used fictitiously, and any resemblance to actual persons, living or dead, business establishments, events or locales is entirely coincidental.

Printed in the USA.

Cover Design and Interior Format
© KILLION
THE
GROUP, INC.

THE GIFT OF BLACK ISLE

OF

HIGHLAND HEALERS 5

KEIRA MONTCLAIR

CHAPTER ONE

Early December 1294, The Black Isle of Scotland

TORCALL MASSIE SCANNED the landscape around the small group he was escorting along the coastline of Beauly Firth on Black Isle. He took his job protecting Tara Matheson and her sister Riley Cameron seriously. They'd come from the faerie glen, one of their favorite destinations for their daily rides. It would be nearly dusk when they arrived back at Eddirdale Castle, seat of the Matheson clan, the brisk night air a warning to hurry back.

Riley had an unusual ability to communicate with the dead, and she'd sensed ghosts at the faerie glen in the past.

The sisters chattered as they often did. Torcall ignored them, not wanting to intrude on their private conversation. Though with the company of not only Torcall but two other guards, Timm and the newcomer Hairalt, it was hardly a private conversation.

Riley's horse, normally a steady mount, slowed and rose onto its hind legs.

"Whoa there!" Torcall reached over to grab the reins of her horse before it tossed Riley onto the dirt path. "Riley?"

He looked at her in concern. Her eyes stared above him as if he weren't there, a glazed look making her appear haunted by something.

Or someone.

"She's having one of her spells," Tara said. "Speak and move calmly, but catch her if you must, Torcall."

"Riley?" he queried as he brought her horse to a standstill. She didn't move. "Timm, you and Hairalt stay behind her in case she falls."

The spell lasted only a few moments. The glaze left her eyes, and she blinked, then stared straight at Torcall.

"Riley? Are you back with us? Can you take the reins?"

She did as he suggested but kept her eyes on him. "'Tis because of you, Torcall."

He nearly fell off his horse. "What do you mean?"

Tara stroked her sister's arm. "I'll speak with her later. She is often confused right after she has a spell. It could mean naught at all." Tara's words did not ease his mind. Whatever Riley had meant, he didn't like the sound of it at all.

The horse's actions were because of him? Or her spell was because of him? The questions would nag at him until he could find out more.

But Torcall had a job to do—get Tara and Riley back to Eddirdale safely. So he nodded, moving along as if naught had happened, and allowed

Tara to take care of Riley as she found her way back to the present after her vision.

It wasn't long before they reached Matheson land, and he shouted when they neared the castle to make sure the gates were open. Timm jumped down from his horse to assist the ladies and hold the horses, and Torcall called someone out from the stable to help.

Tara waved to him. "Help me get her down, please? She's often weak in the knees after her spells."

Torcall reached up to help the younger woman dismount, his hands spanning her narrow waist. He'd never been so close to her before, and he took a moment to admire her. Riley and Tara were quite different in appearance. Riley was more willowy than her sister, her long, wavy hair darker. She kept her tresses plaited, but strands always escaped their tether and fell forward to frame her face. She was a lovely lass, but as far as he knew, no one had ever sought to court her.

He'd overheard several guards speak of her, especially because she was so comely, but they dismissed her just as quickly, fearing her connection to the dead. People in the land of the Scots were used to seers, but not people who could see beyond the veil of death. Most people gave her a wide berth, and none wished to get so close as to be her suitor.

Riley's mystical abilities didn't bother Torcall—he'd seen the good her visions could bring—but they had no future together, no matter how much he admired her. Riley was only here visiting her sister and would head home to Cameron land soon, and it was a trek from Black Isle. He might escort her back, and she would surely visit her sister once or twice a year, but that would be the limit of any time he might spend with Riley Cameron.

When her feet touched the ground, he couldn't help but whisper, "What did you mean when you said it was because of me?"

Riley gave him an odd look. "'Twas no' about you at all. I did no' think you were so conceited, Torcall. Did I say the spell was because of you?"

Torcall smiled. "Aye, you did. Right after it happened."

"Well, I was mistaken. Think no more of it. My thanks for your escort."

Torcall nodded, and Tara approached, laced her arm through Riley's, and the two left for the keep, Riley leaning on her sister and moving slowly. Torcall scratched his head, wondering if he'd imagined her words.

Marcas crossed the courtyard to him and asked, "Is Riley well? It appears she had another spell, aye?"

"Aye, Chief." Torcall gave his full attention to Marcas Matheson, laird of Clan Matheson. He and his two brothers continued the work of rebuilding the clan after a deliberate act of poisoning had killed more than half their clan before the source was discovered. Everyone on Black Isle called the incident "the curse." It had been more than a year now, and every Matheson still carried the shadow of their losses.

Torcall's father and sister had both passed on. His mother lived, but she had never truly recovered from her grief.

Marcas had lost more than most, including his first wife and both his parents. The tragedy had given him his position as the clan's new chieftain. It had been a challenge to save the clan and rebuild it, but Marcas and his brothers had done an admirable job, and each had acquired a wife along the way. The joy of those weddings had done as much as anything could to return strength and life to Clan Matheson.

He'd watched the three men with their new wives, their happiness always overshadowing their hard work.

Brigid, Marcas's wife, was carrying and due around Christmas time, and Jennet's bairn would arrive shortly after. Watching the couples had made him long for a companion of his own.

Perhaps the curse had taken his one chance at marriage away from him.

"Torcall? D'ye hear me, man?" Marcas's voice pulled him back from his memories. "What was her vision about?"

"She didn't say. Tara said to leave her be for the time being. It does take her some time to make sense of what she's seen."

"She didn't fall from her horse, did she?"

"Nay, I was next to her and grabbed her horse's reins when it startled. I managed to catch her before she fell." Torcall realized in that moment that he hadn't noticed catching her. But he had as if it were the most natural thing in the world.

Almost as if he'd known he needed to be close and alert. It had all happened so quickly.

"Good job, Torcall."

Marcas watched him for a moment, a speculative look in his eye. "Have you ever thought of courting Riley? You two are well suited. You're the steadiest man I know, and that seems just what she needs. And 'tis time for you to marry. I know you had hopes before the curse, but you must let thoughts of Violet go, lad."

"I don't think of her any longer, Chief. I did at first, but as my mother says, it serves no purpose." He hated lying to his laird, but telling the truth would serve no purpose either. But he and Riley? "Riley will be returning to Cameron land soon. It hasn't seemed worth considering."

Marcas grinned and leaned down to whisper in his ear. "Change her mind like the rest of us did with our loves." Then he waggled his brows and moved on. "Think on it," he called back over his shoulder.

Torcall moved over to the gates, ready to start his shift on the curtain wall. Alvery, Timm's sire and one of the leaders of the Matheson guards, met him at the foot of the steps up to the battlements.

"You're looking glum for a man who just saved a beautiful lady from a serious fall from her horse, or so Timm says. And what's this of her blaming it on you?"

They climbed the stair together, moving toward the positions that would allow them to best keep watch on the area around the castle.

"She said something about it being my fault

just as she was coming out of her spell, but when we reached the castle, she denied saying anything. Said it had naught to do with me."

"Did Marcas have any ideas?"

"Nay," Torcall replied, shaking his head a wee bit too vigorously. His reaction was more to Marcas's suggestion that he court Riley than Alvery's question.

"He chatted with you for a while. 'Tis unusual for Marcas to slow down for any reason when he is on the way to check on Brigid. What did he want?"

"Just to be sure Riley was hale. Naught more." Alvery gave him a look that said he doubted Torcall's answer, but Torcall didn't rise to the bait. "I'll take the first circuit of the wall."

Alvery nodded, and Torcall started his patrol along the wall gratefully. He didn't need anyone else questioning him about Riley Cameron. If they did, he would surely betray his true feelings for the lass.

He could easily fall in love with her, but he knew the situation was hopeless. None of the lasses on Black Isle would ever show any interest in him. They all knew he'd had strong feelings for Violet MacMahon before the curse. Then the curse had taken her life, leaving him heartbroken. But no one knew the truth of the matter, the part he'd never confess to anyone.

He'd killed Violet.

Unfortunately, God knew.

CHAPTER TWO

R ILEY CAMERON ROLLED her eyes at her sister when she removed her mantle and her scarf after she stepped inside the keep. "How badly did I embarrass myself in front of Torcall, Timm, and Hairalt?" She wouldn't admit to her sister that Torcall was the only one she was concerned about. She'd only mentioned the other two so Tara wouldn't be suspicious of her feelings.

She didn't wish to look like a fool in front of Torcall, the most handsome guard in Eddirdale Castle. On all of Black Isle, truly.

She was grateful to have an excuse to retreat to her bedchamber. Tara followed her up the stairs. Once in the privacy of her chamber, Riley dropped onto the bed and let the tears fall. She was too exhausted to stop them, and her head throbbed with the pain that often came after her visions.

"Riley, what happened? You don't usually cry after a spell." Tara sat next to her and took her hands inside her two. "You're cold. Over by the hearth with you, and I'll stir up the fire."

Riley was too tired to argue. She removed her boots then padded over to the hearth, shivering while her sister put more wood in the fireplace and stirred the embers from gentle glow to warming flame. Sparks leapt about, catching Riley's gaze.

"You still have not said why you are crying, sister." Tara gave her that older sister look, the one where her eyebrows nearly met in the middle to become one line.

"I'm just tired." She wasn't quite ready to reveal everything going on in her mind yet.

"Would you like to sleep?"

"That's not the kind of tired I am." She hated to complain, but she couldn't help it this one time. Her mother always told her that her ability was special, that the angels had deemed her special when they'd granted her this ability of speaking with the dead, but sometimes, she had a hard time considering it a blessing. Sometimes it was more of an annoyance, a penance for something she'd done wrong. Of course, if not for her ability, Tara might not be happily married to Shaw. Her ability to see and speak with a dead horse who needed help had brought Shaw to the truth of crimes that had taken place years ago.

She'd told him many times to stop thanking her, that it was the universe or the angels or God he should thank. Not her. She was just there to deliver the message.

But Shaw didn't see it that way, and neither did her mother.

"What kind of tired are you?" Tara asked.

"Tired of my special skills. Of having my days interrupted by things that I'm to interpret, yet sometimes have no idea of their purpose or their meaning. I'm tired of people staring at me, feeling sorry for me, or looking at me as if I'm the strangest person in the village. I wish to just hide from everyone. Why was I chosen for this?" She set her forehead in her hand, trying to ease her aching head.

Tara finished with the fire then sat down next to her sister, taking her hand again. "What brought this on? You usually are not this discouraged."

Riley wiped her eyes and blew her nose in a linen square. "I'm not sure," she mumbled.

"Aye, you know why. Tell me. I cannae help you if you are not honest with me."

"Oh, Tara, you always could see through me. I've watched you and so many of our cousins marry, and I see how happy you all are with your new loves. Brigid is so in love she sees no one but Marcas when he's within sight. And then there is Jennet. I did no' think she'd ever find someone to match her, but Ethan is perfect for her. They are both so different, yet they are the same. And I've never seen Padraig happier than when he and Gisela visited. And you." She paused to squeeze her sister's hand. "I've never seen you so happy."

Tara looked at her sideways. "Why does that upset you?"

The tears came back with a force. "Because I'm jealous. Soooo jealous," she wailed. "I'll never find someone for myself because no one wishes to be around me. Who would marry someone who can speak with the dead? No one!" She reached for another linen square. "I'll never have bairns. Brigid and Jennet are about to have their firsts, and I'd wager you are carrying already and don't know it yet."

"And if that happens, look how many nieces, nephews, and cousins you'll have to love."

"Not funny. Forget I said anything. I'm just tired." She moved back to her bed, donned her night rail, and climbed in. "I'll take a wee nap, and then I'll feel better."

There was no reason to stay awake. Perhaps she wouldn't feel so hopeless about the one man she admired most ever returning her feelings if she took a nap first. But then again, Torcall had never shown any interest in her, and after today, why would he start now?

She wished she could see for herself how she looked when she had a spell, when she fell backwards. How her eyes rolled back into her head, as people who witnessed her spells often told her happened.

Nay, she'd never wish to see something like that. If she saw what she really looked like, she'd probably hide forever.

She slept fitfully. All she dreamed of was Torcall's face when he kept her from falling off her horse. She awakened in the deep dark of the night, and was surprised she'd slept so long. Tara lay in the chamber's second bed, which she hadn't expected. They had shared a chamber for years as lasses. Now that Tara had married, however, she preferred to lie in Shaw's arms every night.

"You're awake," Tara whispered.

"I am. I'm sorry you felt the need to stay with me instead of sleeping in your husband's arms. I know 'tis where you prefer to be." The beds were so close that she could reach across the empty space and grasp her sister's hand. "But I'm glad you're here. I do miss you in the middle of the night."

"I miss you too." Tara smiled that bright smile that had warmed Riley's days for as long as she could remember. Tara was four years older than Riley's two and twenty summers.

"Now I know you are saying that just to make me feel better. I know you prefer to be in Shaw's bed."

"'Tis true for many reasons," Tara said, rolling onto her back and staring up at the beams in the ceiling. "He is verra warm on a cold night. I don't need the hearth with him next to me. And well, as you know, I enjoy our coupling as husband and wife, but…"

"There is a *but*? Please tell me so I'll feel better that you are here instead of with your husband."

"Sometimes his arm falls across my chest, and then I cannae move. I have to pinch him to make him move his arm so I can breathe again."

"Truly? He sleeps that soundly?" She tried to act serious but failed, giggling instead at the vision of Shaw locking her sister down in their bed so that she couldn't move.

"Och, aye. And when he drinks too much ale, he falls asleep on his back and snores enough to shake the castle." Tara imitated Shaw, outstretching her arms and letting out a loud snore.

Riley giggled, and Tara demonstrated two other sorts of snores. "They can be verra different."

"Oh, Tara. You make me laugh. Poor Shaw."

"Poor Shaw? Poor me! Sometimes he lets gas out in his sleep. I wake up in a fog of rank smell and wonder what he ate. The first time he did it, I told him to stop, and he jumped up and grabbed his sword, shouting, 'Who's there?' He had no idea he'd done anything. I felt bad for waking him up. So now I just bear it. Though someday I'll wear a kerchief across my face to block the fumes."

"Does he no' sleep in the nude?"

"Aye, no trews, no tunic, just Shaw's wild hair and a sword in front of him. He's lucky he didnae hurt himself."

Riley couldn't stop laughing over the image. "Och, Tara, I'll miss you so when I go home."

Tara rolled onto her side and looked over at Riley. "You don't have to go home. You can stay here for a while. We all found men here. Why shouldn't you?"

"There are no more Mathesons to choose."

"There are many guards though, and some of them are very fine. Mayhap we should help you choose someone. Would you like our help?"

"All of you? Nay. Mayhap just yours."

"All right, then. I'll help you find a good one. And then we can take a trip to introduce him to Mama and Papa." Tara fell back into bed. "Now that we've decided that, I'm going back to sleep. I do miss Shaw's hairy leg leaning against mine.

'Tis a comfort to know he's always there to protect me."

"He'll protect you with his life forever. He adores you, Tara."

Now if she could only find someone who felt the same about her.

CHAPTER THREE

TORCALL SAUNTERED TOWARD the lists. He'd just finished his morning guard duty on the wall, and all he'd been able to think of was Riley Cameron. He was glad he'd been able to help during her spell after the visit to the faerie glen, but her remark about *something* being because of him would not leave his mind. Had Violet contacted Riley?

And if so, why?

He'd had feelings for Violet when the curse hit, but he now recognized them for a young man's fancy, nothing that would have lasted. Nothing as deep and aching as his feelings for Riley. Riley was gifted and smart and beautiful, and she had a way of making him laugh. Violet had been serious all the time. In fact, she'd often looked sad whenever he chatted with her.

If Riley had seen Violet, it wasn't because his former crush wished to profess her undying love for him or keep him out of the arms of another woman. Her message was more likely to be his biggest fear—that he'd been the cause of Violet's death. He wiped the sweat from his brow just thinking on the situation.

He knew the truth of the matter, that the poison had come from the well. But what if he hadn't gotten her something to drink when she'd been so sleepy? Would she still be alive?

When he finally made it to the gates of Heaven, would God consider him guilty? His mother had been so religious that she had hammered into his brain that the Lord saw everything he did. Would He remember Torcall's part in Violet's death?

Would Violet be standing next to God tattling on Torcall?

"Massie, join me for the midday meal?" Shaw came up from behind him, placing his hand on Torcall's shoulder. "No need to go to the lists if you just finished your time on the wall."

Lost in thought, he just nodded and turned toward the keep without giving Shaw much thought.

Shaw lowered his voice from his usual loud tone. "Massie, what bothers you so? I've not seen you so worried in an age."

"Naught. I know not what you mean. I am fine." He turned away and hoped Shaw wouldn't read the lie in his eyes. Vainly, it turned out.

"The expression on your face says otherwise. You cannot lie to an old friend," Shaw winked at him and leaned close. "And I think I know your problem." His voice dropped as he glanced over his shoulder as if to be certain he'd not be overheard. "You are dying to kiss the lass, but you don't know quite how to do it. I will be happy to help you out in this situation."

"What situation is that, brother?" Marcas joined him, making them both start because Marcas caught up to them without either of them noticing, running hard from the lists.

"'Tis time for merrymaking. Mayhap we should have a Yuletide celebration to start the season out with a bang. Torcall needs to find a lass to kiss, and a celebration is the best opportunity. Do you not agree, Marcas?" Shaw winked at his brother, breaking into a wide grin.

Shaw's grin told Torcall his friend would not rest until he got his way. There'd be some revelry at Eddirdale Castle within a few days.

Marcas thought for a moment, then said, "I think 'tis a wonderful idea. My poor wife is suffering from back pains, and I think it could be just the thing to take her mind off this wee bairn plaguing her."

"There you go. A festival to celebrate the upcoming birth of another Matheson. Perhaps another heir to the lairdship." Shaw clapped Torcall's shoulder. "And perfect timing for you to find yourself a lass."

Torcall kept mum, not wanting either Shaw or Marcas to know his true feelings about Riley. At least, no more than they already suspected.

Marcas hurried into the hall. "I'll go find my wife. She'll love your idea, Shaw."

And right on cue, Shaw pounced, pulling him off to the side before they entered the keep. "It's Riley on your mind, aye? She's a sweet lass. Think you she would reject you? Because I don't. I've seen her watching you, and she looks quite happy to do so. What are you afraid of?"

"I'm no' afraid. I like Riley, but I'm not sure if she feels the same. I'd rather not become the laughingstock of the clan when she rejects me. And besides, Tara thinks she'll be heading home soon. I don't wish to woo a lass who is leaving within a sennight. I'd be the fool then, do you no' agree?"

"I'll have a wee chat with my wife, see if she'll give me any clues to Riley's feelings. I'll ask her if her sister is interested in anyone here and how she feels about returning to Cameron land."

"Please do no' mention my name. See what Tara says. Promise me you'll say naught to embarrass me."

Shaw chuckled. "Fine, I promise."

Marcas appeared out of nowhere again. Torcall cursed to himself. He had to be more observant. "Did I just hear you ask my brother to ask his wife something, Massie? You'll never get your answer, if you rely on Shaw as your go-between."

Shaw whirled to confront his brother, an amused scowl on his face. "What the hell does that mean, Marcas?"

Marcas chortled. "It means one look at your wife's bosom or her swaying hips, and you can only think of bedding her. Every other thought flies right out of your head. Think you no one else notices?"

"Not true, brother."

Torcall snorted. "I think there might be some truth in it."

"You're in good company, Shaw. We're all the same way with our own wives. You love Tara and don't mind showing it. Naught wrong with that."

Tara stepped out into the courtyard from the larder as if she knew they were talking about her. Shaw's head turned so fast that Torcall couldn't help but laugh. Shaw didn't react to his laughter, never even heard it, if Torcall was any judge, proving the truth of Marcas's words.

Torcall fell silent. He couldn't help but wish he might share the same fate as his laird and his brothers—find a wife he loved so truly that he couldn't think properly when she was around.

Shaw grinned and watched his wife cross the courtyard away from them, her hips swaying. She glanced back over her shoulder and flashed her husband a private smile.

Torcall wished it were Riley gifting him with a smile and a sway of her hips.

Riley dressed carefully in her chamber the next evening. Tara had returned to the bedchamber she shared with Shaw, and Riley didn't blame her. She would do the same if she married someone she liked half so much as Tara liked Shaw.

But who would she find to marry?

A knock sounded at the door. "Enter."

Jennet came in, closing the door quietly behind her. Her blonde hair was already neatly braided, and she wore a rich green gown for the evening's festivities. "How are you, Riley? You've been quiet the last few days. Are you still unsettled by your visit to the faerie glen?"

Riley lied to her cousin. "Nay, I'm fine. There was naught clear about the vision, so I'm unsure how to interpret it."

"Will you go back and see if you can learn more?" Jennet found a stool near the hearth and sat.

She shrugged, doing her best to weave her fingers through her unruly waves to untangle them. "I had not planned on it, but I'm sure Tara will insist on it."

Jennet moved over to the bed behind Riley and said, "Take a step back and I'll fix your hair. I have the perfect implement. I'll straighten your waves and just pull the top part of your hair back, braid it there. Like Connor's wife Sela does."

"The Norse way?"

"Aye, and Dyna has followed her mother's style. I like it. Better than one big one. It stays in place better. She showed me some different ways of interweaving the plaits that make truly lovely patterns."

Riley stepped into place so Jennet could reach her hair. "I'd love to see what you can do with it. I have to admit I miss having Mama around to plait my hair."

"We all miss our mamas. We love our husbands, but Mamas fuss over us. And I'm sure your mama misses you, since you left her without either of her daughters. My mother has Lily and her lassies and Bethia and Torrian and Gregor's girls.

So many that sometimes I wonder if she even notices I'm gone."

Riley thought of the large brood of bairns and grandbairns at Ramsay Castle. "Aye, you have as many at Ramsay Castle as Aunt Maddie has at Grant Castle. I think Mama is often jealous."

"Your brood will grow soon," Jennet said, pulling a comb gently through Riley's tresses. "Brin will be looking for a wife soon, and as heir to the chief, he'll have many to choose from. But I've been expecting Aunt Jennie to arrive any day since both of her lassies are here. Do you no' expect her?"

"Nay, my mother won't leave Papa without a good reason. And she keeps so busy with her healing duties. Just as you and Tara do, especially with Brigid taking on less as she gets closer to her time."

"You truly do no' expect her?"

"Nay. Why do you say so?" Jennet was one of the wisest people Riley knew. Perhaps she needed to pay more attention to her predictions.

"She might be afraid you would find someone here, and she'd lose both you and Tara to Black Isle. Surely she would wish for you to find someone closer to home. She won't want all her grandbairns born here."

Riley hadn't given that much thought. Her mother wouldn't want them both here, with that she had to agree.

"Which do you prefer, Riley? Black Isle or Cameron land?" Jennet finished fussing with her waves and stepped up to plait a section on one side of Riley's head.

"I don't know. I like both." At the moment, with her new interest in Torcall, she preferred Black Isle.

"Think you to go home alone? Will you enjoy it the same?" Jennet asked.

Riley thought for a moment. "I think mayhap Tara and I could be the same as you and Brigid."

Jennet looked puzzled. "What do you mean?"

"I don't think anyone is surprised that you and Brigid both decided to stay on Black Isle. You've always been so close that no one ever thought you would separate."

Jennet tipped her head and shrugged her shoulders. "They were no' wrong. Brigid and I have spent near as much time together as sisters."

Riley stared at the door as if she expected it to open. "I missed Tara desperately before I came to Black Isle. Do you think Mama noticed?"

"I suspect so. Mothers see more than they let on, I'm sure. My mother knew I would stay here when Brigid married Marcas."

"Funny that you three were kidnapped by Marcas. 'Tis still one of my favorite stories to tell. So romantic, especially for Brigid and Marcas." It was one of the best stories ever, almost rivaling some of her parents' stories.

"I agree. There was something between them from the first time we stopped in the forest on our way here. They'd only known each other for mere hours, and Marcas abducted us, but I could tell there was something between them."

"Did you feel the same with Ethan?"

"Aye. I noticed him and the way he was. He was more like me than any other man I'd ever met."

When Marcas lost his wife and saw his daughter sickened as a result of the curse, he'd led Shaw and Ethan on a mission to steal the most renowned healers in all the land, Jennie Cameron and Brenna Ramsay. Knowing the healers only by reputation and not by sight, the Matheson brothers returned to Black Isle not with the healers they were seeking, but their daughters Tara and Jennet and Jennet's cousin Brigid.

"The oddest part is that you came along willingly, Jennet. Did you ever wonder why?" Riley asked.

"Nay. Brigid and I have always worked together. When Marcas grabbed her, it just made sense for me to come too. There is a lesson in this for you, Riley." Jennet finished her hair and stood in front of her cousin to admire her work. She smiled in approval. "The braids suit you perfectly."

"What lesson?"

"If you feel drawn to someone, you should follow your instincts. There are always angels about who are trying to tell you which way to go. They'll point you in the right direction."

"I'm surprised you believe that, Jennet. Brigid might say it, but you are more serious minded."

"Tales from my mother. She says angels brought Uncle Alex and Aunt Maddie through that storm one Christmas. She has convinced me. So the question is, who are you drawn to? Someone here or on Cameron land?"

Riley ducked her head to hide her blush, but she was saved from confessing the truth when the door burst open.

Tara hurried in. "Come, dear sister. The celebration has begun! Oh, you do look beautiful! Jennet, you did a lovely job with her hair. Come downstairs, both of you."

They stepped into the passageway and moved toward the staircase. When Riley glanced down, the first face she saw made her heart skip a beat.

Torcall Massie.

CHAPTER FOUR

TORCALL'S MOUTH TURNED dry with one look at the stunning beauty at the top of the stairs, her appearance as regal as if she sat on the highest throne. Her gown was a forest green with golden ribbons on the bodice, and it hugged her curves in all the right places. He swallowed hard, willing himself to look away, but he could not, the queen at the peak commanding his attention. He was her most loyal subject. Riley paused, caught his gaze for a moment, then looked away, gracefully moving down the staircase as everyone watched her descend behind Jennet and Tara.

His gaze scanned the area, surprised to see everyone's eyes on Riley when Jennet was so obviously with child, her gowns hiding the bairn as if only a few months along when he'd heard Ethan say it could be less than a moon before she delivered her bairn. Since Brigid was the healer who cared for most of the expectant mothers, they could keep everything a secret. But no one noticed at present.

Clearly, Riley's beauty caught everyone else nearly the same as it did him.

She paused at the bottom of the staircase, glancing at the group gathered for the evening's festivities. Perhaps two dozen people milled around the hall, with more out in the courtyard. Riley and Tara made their way through them to join Shaw's small cluster.

Torcall had been too immobilized to approach her before she moved. Too lost in her aura.

Her long dark waves had been plaited in a way he'd never seen before, one large braid down her back with two smaller braids wound through her hair in an intricate pattern. He liked her hair when it was long and free, simply because it was always different, the strands floating behind her when she was on horseback. But this pattern was also appealing. With her hair off her face, he was able to appreciate her strong cheekbones, full pink lips, and brown eyes. Riley's eyes saw more than anyone else could ever see.

An elbow to his back caught him short.

"If you keep staring, everyone will know what you are about." Alvery stood next to him, a hint of a smile on his face. He waggled his brow at his friend. "She is a beauty and no' attached to anyone. Why no' approach her?"

He sighed, angry with himself that his feelings had been so evident on his face. "I think she's pretty. 'Tis all you need to know. Naught more."

"Surely you jest." Alvery coughed and said, "Don't wait too long, or ye'll lose your chance. I'm heading over for a share of that venison. Do as you like." His friend clasped his shoulder, then crossed the room.

His friend might not see them, but there were reasons he and Riley would not suit. Her father was a nobleman and laird. She was a beauty with a talent unlike any other, and wise beyond her years.

He was naught more than a guard, with none but a guard's practical, everyday skills.

Riley could speak with the dead. Others were seers, but no one he'd ever heard of could speak with the dead. She should be in the king's court, using her talent to help others.

Or perhaps she should live in an abbey, helping those who came for spiritual guidance. She could travel to Europe, to France, help so many with her gift. The possibilities were endless.

Torcall would always be a guard for the Mathesons, traveling off Black Isle only as part of his duty to protect Marcas and his family. He looked toward Riley, where she stood laughing with Tara and Shaw at the fireplace. Then his vision blurred, and the image before him was of Riley on the floor, her eyes closed, her brown waves fanned out in a circle around her head. He bit back a cry.

She looked dead.

He blinked, and the image left him as quickly as it had come. He sucked in a breath and looked around to see if anyone else had noticed anything, noticed his changed gaze. Did the vision mean something? He was no seer, so where had it come from?

Was Riley in danger?

He fastened his eyes on her, and she glanced at him as she filled a cup with warm wine from the hearth. Her smile soothed his fear and made his heart race at the same time.

Marcas came up behind him and spoke to him in a low voice. "You would make a fine couple, in my eyes. Brigid agrees. Talk with her."

He couldn't lie to his laird, so instead he changed the subject. "Is Brigid no' well? I have no' seen her tonight."

"She's a wee bit weak in the belly. She ate too much earlier, and now the wee bairn is telling her so. She'll be fine. I don't know how the lasses can carry on for so long with such a weight attached to their midsection. Surely the extra mound should tire them out, but naught stops Brigid except her weak stomach. I told her to stay abed for once. I'll only be here for a short time, then I'll find some treats to tempt her and join her abovestairs."

"I hope she feels better, Chief."

Shaw called out to Marcas. "Brother, I need your opinion. Join us, please."

"Talk to Riley," Marcas said with a nod as he headed for his brother's group.

The new guard Hairalt entered the hall, his gaze searching the area, slowing when he saw Riley, but then finally falling on Torcall and crossing the room to him.

"I did no' expect to see so many here," Hairalt said. "'Tis winter and there's a large crowd in the courtyard as if it were summer. The clan has a great spirit for entertainment."

Torcall shrugged and said, "I've naught to compare it to, but we do have spirit, especially since the end of the curse. We're grateful, I believe. Not so with the Miltons?" Hairalt had recently asked to join Matheson clan, with the blessing of the Milton chieftain. He said he wished to bolster the growing clan, and apparently Milton did not mind. And truly, the Mathesons were still shorthanded, so Marcas had welcomed the guard.

"Nay, only those invited. 'Tis one of the reasons I wished to leave. I'd heard the guards were included here, so I wished to move on."

"No family in the Milton clan?" Torcall asked. Most people didn't switch clans, especially guards. Family loyalties ran strong on Black Isle, and he was curious about Hairalt's wish to change allegiance.

"Nay. I had family at Clan Ross, but they all caught the fever and died. I could no' bear to stay there, so I shifted to the Miltons. But Clan Milton did no' feel right to me. Clan Matheson suits me better. 'Tis smaller."

"I understand your situation. I lost my father and sister to the curse, but I cannot imagine leaving the Mathesons, even if my mother didn't still live here. I hope you'll stay on. We can use as many guards as possible." He'd also lost the lass he fancied to the curse, but Hairalt didn't need to know about Violet.

"Saints above. Is that Riley Cameron with the

wildly plaited hair?" Hairalt's eyes widened as he stared at Riley.

Torcall bristled. "Aye, but she's no' for you. She's shown you no favors, has she?"

Hairalt chuckled. "She just hasn't had the chance to know me. I'm going to invite her for a stroll." After running his hand through his wavy, fair hair, Hairalt nodded to him. "Wish me luck!"

It took every ounce of willpower Torcall had not to put himself between Hairalt and Riley, or even command him to leave the hall.

If Riley was to be wooed by anyone here, it would be Torcall. No one would impose on the woman he was falling in love with.

No one.

Riley did her best not to stare at Torcall, but it was difficult. His hair was a light brown, and she knew it had streaks of gold in it when the sun hit it. His eyes matched his hair. A golden bronze, she thought. He was by far the handsomest man here, and while he was pleasing to her eyes, her mother had taught her well about not staring.

She turned her back to him so she wouldn't be tempted to focus on him. "Tara, how is Brigid?" She hadn't seen their cousin all evening, and she hoped everything was well with her wee bairn. Both her mother, Jennie, and her aunt Brenna, Jennet's mother, had said Brigid would deliver near Yule, and Jennet shortly after. She couldn't wait to see whether they would have lads or lassies.

"She's fine, just a bit sick in her belly. Brigid is quite happy to stay abed," Tara said with a knowing smile. "We don't see that often, do we, Jennet?"

"Brigid has been happy to stay abed of late," Jennet said. "It makes me believe she is closer to her time than even her mother thinks. I check on her often." Jennet and Brigid had been inseparable as they grew up, following Jennet's mother around, learning healing skills as much as they could. Jennet and Tara were healers for the Matheson clan now, and often the Miltons. Brigid was so busy with Marcas's bairns and her duties inside the castle that she rarely practiced her healing skills, except when someone called for help delivering bairns.

Tara gave a quick scowl, but then smiled effortlessly. Riley knew that look of her sister's.

"What is it?" she asked.

"Someone is heading straight for you, sister. I think it's the new guard from our ride the other day. I don't recall his name. Hush now."

An arm snaked around Riley's waist, startling her despite Tara's warning. Why would he touch her? That was totally unexpected. She took a step away, wishing she'd be greeting Torcall instead of the new blond guard from Clan Milton.

"Greetings to all the fair ladies of Clan Matheson. I'm Hairalt and at your service. Though pleased to meet you all, I'd be lying if I did no' tell you that I wish to make this lovely lady's acquaintance first." His arm still rested on her hip as he turned to face Riley.

To her surprise, Torcall appeared beside Hairalt, his eyes intent on the other man. "You have no right to touch her. Matheson guards treat all women with respect, and she's a chieftain's daughter. Take your hand away."

As if Torcall's gaze had physical force, Hairalt stepped away from Riley.

Riley caught Tara's fast grin and widened eyes. Her dear sister even took a step back, another move Riley knew well. Tara wished to see how this would play out, and Jennet followed her.

That left Riley standing between two men.

Torcall stood fast and raised his chin, his experience and authority as a trusted Matheson guard apparent in his bearing. "Apologize to the lady, Hairalt."

"I'll not apologize. She did no' seem to mind at all." Hairalt leaned closer and whispered something in Riley's ear. Then he laughed, taunting Torcall. Torcall couldn't hear what he said, but Riley blushed so quickly that he needed to defend her, but he was still in his chieftain's hall so he had to consider his actions carefully.

To his surprise, the fool pushed it even more. Hairalt came closer to him and taunted, "Are you tough enough to do anything about it?" Then the daft man shoved him.

He dared to push him in the middle of Matheson hall where everyone was watching.

Torcall couldn't have stopped himself if he had tried.

He plowed his fist right into Hairalt's face.

CHAPTER FIVE

RILEY SQUEALED WHEN she heard the crack of bone as Torcall's fist connected with the blond man's face.

"Oh my!" Her hand flew to cover her mouth in shock. Torcall pulled his fist back to swing again, so Riley quickly stepped in and grabbed his wrist. "Torcall, stop!"

"He touched you!" His eyes shone with a fury unlike anything she'd ever seen. "He has no right to touch you."

The hall fell silent at the raised voices. Jennet barked out a laugh unlike anything Riley had ever heard, loud in the shocked hush of the room, and she spun to stare at her cousin. "Why is this funny?"

Jennet sobered quickly, covered her mouth with her hand, stared at the floor, and said, "Naught. Naught you need to know now. I'll explain later. In private."

Her sister, blast her, also stood back with a wide grin and a sparkle in her eyes that told her all she needed to know. Tara was thoroughly enjoying herself.

Then Marcas was there and a moment later, his brother Shaw.

"What happened, Massie?" He placed both hands on Torcall's broad shoulders and pushed him a few steps away from the group.

Riley turned toward Hairalt, who stood with a strange, sideways smile on his face. "I'm so sorry this happened." As the scene settled, the others in the hall returned to their own conversations, and Riley breathed a sigh of relief.

Marcas turned to Riley, his hands still on Torcall. "Riley, would you care to tell me what happened?"

She glanced at Torcall, his face still flushed with anger, but he seemed to have regained his normal control. She squared her shoulders and explained, "Hairalt came up behind me and greeted us, and me in particular. He…" she faltered with her words, unsure of how to describe Hairalt's demeanor and Torcall's reaction.

He'd been angry that Hairalt had touched her. Did she dare repeat that to Marcas?

"And?" Marcas asked, waiting for her response.

"And Torcall, well, he said…" She frowned, looking at Torcall.

Torcall took a deep breath and steeled his expression. "Do not make her explain for me. Hairalt boldly strode over and wrapped his hand around Riley's waist, an action entirely inappropriate for a man barely acquainted with a lass, especially a chieftain's daughter. It was wrong of him."

Riley whispered, "And Hairalt shoved Torcall first. 'Tis the truth."

Marcas looked at Hairalt. "You were in the wrong, Hairalt. You approached a lass—a nobleman's daughter and a guest of mine—rudely. Apologize."

Riley fumbled for words, blushing a light shade of red. "There's no need, I mean, he does no' have to…"

Marcas raised his hand, and Riley fell silent. "I've issued an order to one of my guards, Riley. I expect him to obey it."

"Aye," Torcall said. "If he wishes for a place here, he must learn what's expected of Matheson guards. He needs to apologize."

Brigid appeared on the balcony, looking down at the group.

"Love?" Marcas asked, striding to the bottom of the staircase. "Is something wrong?"

"Nay," she said, her gaze searching over the entire hall. "I thought I heard my father's bellow. Is he here, Marcas?"

Jennet burst into laughter at the same exact time Tara did, directly behind Jennet. The two hooting and slapping their thighs before hugging each other, tears falling down their cheeks.

Riley was so confused she didn't know what to do or say. Her sister continued to laugh, Marcas was dealing with Brigid, Torcall was calming down, but still angry, and Hairalt merely shrugged his shoulders and walked out of the great hall. Riley decided to go after him to apologize.

Or was it that she just had to get away from

Tara and Jennet and their shared jokes? She was confused by Torcall's actions, his anger, and her sister's reaction. Torcall's anger seemed so extreme compared to Hairalt's infraction. True, she hadn't wanted to be touched by the man, but Torcall had seemed to take more offense than she had herself.

No one noticed her leave. The door closed behind her, and she chased after Hairalt.

"Please wait, Hairalt. I'm so sorry you were hurt."

The guard stopped and turned, his expression quickly growing warm in welcome. He rubbed his cheek and said, "He did no' hurt me. I'll be a wee bit black and blue in a day but think naught of it. He seemed to be anxious to cause trouble."

"Torcall? Nay, he's no' usually like that."

Hairalt's arm snaked around her waist again, and he led her down a path at the periphery of the courtyard to an area near the garden where there was a bench. One torch lit the dark area, but not by much.

"Sit with me for a few moments. I wish to get to know you. 'Tis all I wanted before Torcall interrupted us. Riley Cameron, you are by far the loveliest lass on Matheson land."

Riley blushed at his compliment and accepted his invitation to rest on the bench. Then she couldn't help but wonder if he was flattering her for some reason. She'd never been called the loveliest of anywhere, and never prettier than her sister or her cousins. Brigid was one of the most beautiful lasses she'd ever known. In fact, many of Clan Ramsay often argued about who was the prettiest in all the clan, Brigid's sister Sorcha or Brigid.

"You don't believe me, do you?" Hairalt asked, placing a finger under her chin to lift her face to his. "I would wager you are so beautiful that no man has dared to give you your first kiss. Am I right?"

Staring into his gray eyes, she didn't answer, simply because she would never admit that she was past twenty summers and had never been kissed. She knew it wasn't because of her beauty. He didn't wait long to make a move, his mouth descending to hers, the heat from his lips searing hers into opening of their own accord, without her deciding to do so.

And when his tongue met hers, she pulled back in shock. He smiled. "My apologies, Riley, but I am drawn to you like a stallion to the finest mare in the meadow. Your lips are the sweetest I've ever tasted."

His flattery caught her off guard, and she jumped up from the bench. "Excuse me. I must return to the hall. I'm cold." She strode away, his words following her.

"I'll not forget that kiss nor you. I'll return for more, lass."

She was nearly to the keep when the door flew open, and Torcall stood there. "Riley? Did he force you to go with him? You seem out of sorts. Did he hurt you?"

She heard a step behind her, but she would not turn around to see if it was Hairalt. His voice gave her the answer. "Nay, I did no' hurt her. 'Twas naught more than a sweet kiss."

Torcall's jaw clenched in anger again, and she spoke quickly to prevent a repeat of the scene inside. "Please, Torcall. I'd like to go back to the hall."

"Does he need to apologize to you? Did he take liberties? Because if so, I'll teach him how to act properly when he's with a fine lass." He glared at Hairalt over her shoulder.

She suspected Hairalt sported a wide grin, from the note of humor in his voice. "Until later, Riley Cameron."

The rapping of his boot heels on stone as he walked away was meant to be a statement of power, a message to Torcall that he had no control over him. At least, that was what Hairalt seemed to be about, as if he wished to flaunt his defiance in Torcall's face. She did not want to be caught in the middle of their rivalry, which she feared would turn violent again.

"Torcall?" she whispered, a bit afraid of his anger. "You're scaring me."

Torcall closed his eyes and relaxed his posture. "Forgive me, Riley. I did not wish to make a spectacle of you nor frighten you. I just wished to put him in his place. Please be careful. He is too forward. If he bothers you again, come to me and I'll take care of him. Anytime. He's only here on a trial basis. Marcas can send him away if you wish."

There was only one problem with that.

She didn't wish to be the cause of someone being banned from the clan. A small part of her was pleased because she'd finally had her first kiss. It hadn't sent any butterflies flying through her belly as her sister had told her about her kisses with Shaw, but it was nice to feel as though she'd finally joined the club of womanhood.

"He's fine, Torcall. He did no' hurt me."

"Massie!" Marcas's voice boomed out of the hall.

Torcall spun around.

"I'll see you in my solar for a moment."

Torcall gave Riley a small bow. "I must go."

Riley chewed on the inside of her cheek. She wasn't sure what this evening's events meant. But as Torcall walked away, she felt more alone than ever. Though she wanted to call out to him, she had no idea what she'd say. She couldn't demand that he tell her how he felt about her, after all. And that's really what she wanted to know.

Was there hope, or should she expect to be alone forever?

CHAPTER SIX

TORCALL FOLLOWED MARCAS through the hall and upstairs to his solar. Several people clapped him on the shoulder as he passed, as if congratulating him for confronting Hairalt. He was glad they were pleased, but he wished he knew how Riley really felt about his intervention.

When he closed the door behind him in the solar, he was surprised to see Brigid sitting next to Marcas.

"My lady," he said, bowing slightly toward her.

"Sit down, Torcall," Marcas ordered.

He did as he was instructed and then waited. It wasn't Marcas who addressed him first but Brigid. "Torcall, please do not ever say that again."

Totally confused, he looked to Marcas for guidance. "My lady? What did I say to upset you?"

Marcas smiled, finally letting out a chuckle as he peeked at his wife, who quickly swatted his arm playfully. "'Tis no' funny, husband."

Marcas looked back to Torcall who was still confused. "Torcall, Logan Ramsay's favorite saying is to call someone out for touching Brigid's mother." Everyone knew of Brigid's parents,

Logan and Gwyneth, prior spies for Scotland. Logan was a fierce swordsman and archer while her mother had the reputation as being the best archer in all the land. Better than her father.

"Do you know how many people he's threatened for touching my mother? And for some reason." Her eyes misted. "I'm no' sure why, but you sounded just like my father." Her face paled as she stared at her hands in her lap. He knew Logan Ramsay had a strong personality, but did his own daughter fear him? He didn't know what to say at all, but fortunately, fate took care of that for him.

Before he knew it, Brigid let out a howl and began to sob, her head tipping back as if she were in deep pain. "I want Papa. I miss him."

Marcas said to Torcall, "You may go now. I'm glad you put Hairalt in his place, but I could no' tell you so out there. You have the authority to take whatever action is necessary to discipline him in the future, as well. Go while I calm my wife. She's nearing the end for sure." Marcas lovingly patted her well-rounded belly.

Brigid wailed a bit louder, so Torcall moved toward the door at the same time Marcas stood, lifted his wife, and settled her on his lap. "There, there. Your sire will be here soon enough with your mother. They'll no' miss the birth of our bairn…"

Torcall stepped out, closing the door behind him quietly and wiping the sweat from his brow.

Now what? He looked down from the balcony into the hall, picking out each member of the castle household. Neither Hairalt nor Riley had returned to the feasting.

Instinct deep in his gut told him to find Hairalt and make sure he wasn't bothering any other lasses. Or perhaps he should follow Riley. To protect her from Hairalt, of course.

Or any other male who dared to stare at Riley's lips the way Hairalt had. He raked his hand through his hair, tugging when he thought of the way the bastard had looked at his lass.

His lass.

She wasn't his, though. He'd never even spoken to Riley more than duty required, never told her he thought her the loveliest lass in the castle and that he'd like to know her better. He wondered how he should go about it. Perhaps he should speak to Tara, since her parents weren't here. Or would it be better to approach Riley directly, take her for a stroll as Hairalt had done?

His gaze landed on couple after couple—Tara and Shaw, Jennet and Ethan, and more. These were the times when his lack of a sweetheart was the most difficult. Everyone seemed attached except for the few loners off to the side. Torcall was always one of them. Even with Violet, he hadn't had the nerve to speak to her directly, instead sending her mysterious gifts and hoping she'd figure out they came from him. He just had no idea how to go about courting a lass.

Standing here alone wasn't going to accomplish anything. He went down the stairs and back to the festivities, finding a place by the hearth to continue his ruminations.

He'd watched Marcas and Brigid, but that hadn't been what he would consider courting. Marcas had kidnapped her, she and her cousins had solved the curse, and it seemed once that ended, Marcas had been seen kissing Brigid endlessly until her sire had arrived and threatened to cut Marcas's bollocks off.

Ethan and Jennet had been so secretive that he hadn't even noticed the two had an interest in each other until they'd announced their impending wedding. Ethan had arranged for a place where he could meet Jennet and carry on with no one being the wiser. Torcall didn't wish to follow their example.

Shaw and Tara? Their relationship had seemed to take place on horseback, the two going back and forth between Matheson and Cameron land and the faerie glen. Of course, he hadn't been privy to what happened on Cameron land. But before he knew it, the two were announcing their impending nuptials.

So who could he go to for advice? How he wished his father were here. His mother was not yet over her grief of losing her husband and daughter, so he couldn't confide in her. She would be happy if he married and gave her grandbairns, but getting that far was for him to figure out himself.

Shaw and Tara suddenly appeared in front of him, startling him out of his thoughts. They had the look of people who'd just eaten honey straight from the jar—too sweet by far.

"Greetings to you," he said, his eyes narrowing

in suspicion. He studied Shaw, looking for any inkling of what he was thinking. Then he looked to Tara and saw her satisfied smile. Her lips moved and halted twice before she managed to get any words out.

"Torcall, I've…nay, *we've* noticed you keeping an eye on my sister, and we do appreciate it, but mayhap…" She cleared her throat, glancing at Shaw as if needing his help.

"Take Riley back to the fairy glen," Shaw said.

He couldn't have been more stunned. "Why? Did she ask to return?"

"Nay," Tara said. "But she's never told me what she saw there, and I know she saw something. 'Tis most unusual for her not to tell me. I think she needs a reminder."

"I'd be happy to take her back, but only if 'tis what she wishes," he said.

Tara's face turned as serious as he'd ever seen it. "She'll meet you in the courtyard on the morrow when the sun is high. We'll be there too."

Torcall had a sinking feeling that this wasn't going to be the sweet journey he'd hoped for. He should dread it, rather, though he could dread nothing that put him close to Riley. One name ruined the prospect of a ride to the faerie glen with Riley.

Violet.

How he prayed Riley would never uncover the truth about Violet. If the truth were known, he did not do anything to the lass intentionally, but he wondered what Violet would say. Would she tell him that God blamed him? Or could she possibly say to stop blaming himself? If he were to guess, it would be the former. God watched everything you did, or so his mother claimed. Either way, it was probably best for him to be there if she did indeed speak to Violet.

"I'll be there," he said, "and glad to be of service."

He gave his farewells and stepped out to the courtyard, no longer in the mood to celebrate Yule or anything else. He paused in the chill air for a deep breath and a glimpse of the stars, then decided to go to his mother's cottage rather than spend his night in the guards' quarters. She lived in one of the many huts behind the castle, set farther away from the bay in case of heavy rains and flooding.

Not surprised to find her awake and staring into a cup of mead, he hoped that meant she would be open to a conversation.

"Good eve to you, Mama. You are hale?"

"Aye. Come sit, Torcall. You've been so busy with your guard duties that we hardly chat anymore. I'm so grateful you're here." Tears shone in her eyes, but he pretended not to notice. He plopped into the chair with a sigh, accepting the cup of mead his mother handed him. "Are you hungry, lad?"

"Nay."

"Something is bothering you. What is it?"

"Naught," he said, now that he was here, not wanting to talk about his troubles. But his mother could always read him.

"You've reached the age when a man wants

more in life, I think. Torcall, you need to find a woman to marry. Have bairns of your own. Have you not thought of anyone? I know it was difficult after the curse, but that was a long time ago. Surely there is someone here who pleases you. God would want you happily married. He watches you always."

"Mama, I know you believe all that about God watching everything you do, that He's always looking over your shoulder, but I wish you would stop forcing your beliefs onto me."

"Torcall, why would you say such a thing?" Then her voice dropped to a whisper. "Hush. He can hear you."

"Because mayhap I don't believe everything like you do. Believe what you wish, but please don't try to force your beliefs on me."

"I'll do my best, but you know how I feel. But you still need to marry—for yourself, if not for God."

"I wouldn't know how to go about it." Perhaps it was time to ask someone. "There is a lass, but I know not… How does one court a lass if her father is not around to speak with?"

"Your heart will tell you, my son. It will happen. I met your father, and the next thing I knew he was stealing kisses behind a tree." She smiled as her memory went back to happier times. "But he did ask my father for permission soon after. If you're not sure, ask Alvery or Shaw, even Marcas. He respects you verra much, because you're so strong and steady."

He nodded. She had given him much to think about.

It sounded like what happened to his mother had just happened to Riley, except it had been with a different man—Hairalt.

Was he too late?

CHAPTER SEVEN

BEFORE LEAVING THE Yule celebration, Riley agreed to return to the faerie glen, but only because her sister wouldn't accept her refusal.

And she'd tried to refuse more than once. Though Tara had been all wrapped up in burning the *Cailleach* log to banish the cold of winter, Tara had persisted in trying to convince Riley she needed to go back to the faerie glen.

At one point, she'd said, "Tara, forget the faeries and focus on the winter that the old woman is bringing us. Throw the *Cailleach* log in and forget about the glen."

Tara had been persistent.

"If you wish to have any relationship with Torcall, you must see him every day. I tell you 'tis the only way. Besides, you never told me anything about the last trip to the faerie glen. What did you see in your vision, and why did you tell Torcall it was about him?"

Riley chewed on the inside of her cheek but couldn't come up with a reasonable lie, so she decided the truth would probably be best. "It was a lass who Torcall used to know. She said she died during the curse. 'Tis all I know."

"Why did she come to you?"

Riley just sighed and shook her head. Why did her sister always need to know everything about her visions? Tara had an amazing sense of picking up insights into any of Riley's visions. It was as if they truly did have an odd connection as sisters.

"What was her issue, Riley? Please tell me."

"No serious issue that I know of. She didn't mention her death. She wished to speak with Torcall. I don't recall her name." She hoped to get away with that wee lie. There was no need to share more until they arrived back at the glen, and Torcall should get to decide how much of the visitor's message was shared with Tara or anyone else.

Torcall would hear the truth, whether he wished to or not. After that, it was up to him.

She had avoided her sister since saying goodnight, until they met Shaw and Torcall in the courtyard for the midday outing.

Now the four, plus a small contingent of guards, approached the faerie glen on horseback, and Riley's stomach twisted with anxiety. She'd learn more about the mysterious Violet. She could have asked any of the Mathesons about the young woman, but for some reason, she didn't wish to know anything about her.

Her first vision of the lass had given her a bad feeling, so she'd vowed not to mention anything else until she met with her again.

The faerie glen was located in Rosemarkie, a

lovely, wooded glen a bit inland from the path along the coast. Riley liked it because it was usually lush with greenery. The winter landscape was entirely different, allowing for the whispering of the winds through the pines. She tugged her scarf tighter around her neck, the wind making its way inside her mantle.

She wondered what the faerie glen would bring today. It was home to two waterfalls, and Riley had met ghosts in both areas. Would Violet come back? The closer they came, the more her belly did flip-flops, just because this was all about Torcall.

Once there, Torcall and Shaw dismounted, Shaw giving instructions to the other guards after helping his wife, while Torcall assisted her down from her horse. She smiled, but said nothing else, and she sensed the tension in Torcall's body without even trying, his arms rigid as he lowered her to the ground.

"Torcall, it will be all right." She peered up at him, surprised to see the worry in his eyes.

His jaw clenched at her words, and she knew that this was not a good memory for him. What had happened between Violet and Torcall? She wasn't sure she wished to know, but it was too late to turn back now.

They made their way toward the first waterfall.

Riley's sister stayed close to her side as she led the group of four to the waterfall, where she expected to see the dead person who couldn't rest.

"Ask her for her name this day, would you

please?" Tara gave her that older sister look that said *because I'm telling you to.* Riley had learned to recognize that look a long time ago. She adored her sister, but even her sister had faults. Being nosy was one of them, especially when it came to her special skills.

Shaw drew up on one side of her while Tara stood on the other. Both stared at the waterfall in front of them, the bubbling sound as mesmerizing as the view, at least in her mind. Shaw yelled back, "Get up here, Massie."

Torcall had stopped at the edge of the clearing without Riley noticing. Now his steps were slow, his gaze darting to Riley, then around the glen and back to Riley.

"You are no' afraid of my wife's sister, are you?" Shaw asked with a laugh.

"Nay. But I should be on patrol, making sure no one sneaks up on you. I'll patrol the area on foot while the other guards patrol on horseback." He stepped away while the other three ignored him.

A sudden breeze caught Riley's hair, whipping it back from her face. The winter air warmed, as though an ancient soul wrapped her in a thick fur. She often thought these sensations made her more receptive, more agreeable, or perhaps simply strengthened her skills. Her body hummed with an invisible power, her arms rising to stretch away from her body and her head lifting. She sensed an aura about her just before the trapped soul appeared.

A woman walked out from behind the waterfall, a lovely woman with flaming red hair unlike any Riley had ever seen. It fell in waves to her waist, a shade of red like burnished copper with darker wine-red strands interwoven with the lightest. "Please tell Torcall he must stay." The redhead stopped at the edge of the water. Perhaps the bank of the creek formed a boundary between worlds. "I must speak with him."

"Who are you?" Riley whispered.

"Is someone here?" Tara asked, gripping her sister's hand, staring at the waterfall as if the apparition would appear to her if she stared more intently.

"Aye, but please let me go. Staring at her will not make her appear. I gather from the expression on your face that you can no' see her." Her gaze drifted from Tara to Shaw, then fell on Torcall, who shook his head in denial at her implied question.

"I cannot," Tara replied, looking at her husband.

"Nay, we cannot. Someone we know? Someone from Clan Matheson?"

"A beautiful woman with long red hair that reaches her waist."

Shaw turned to stare at Torcall.

"Who are you?" Riley repeated, louder this time. "I need to know your name, if you please. What is your message?"

The woman smiled. "The message is for my dear friend Torcall, something he must hear. This is so important, but I know he'll deny all. You must convince him. He must make his own decision about what to do, but he will once he learns the truth."

Riley looked at Torcall. "The message is for you, Torcall. She says the truth will help you make a decision."

Torcall whispered, "What does she say?"

The apparition said, "My name is Violet, and the truth isn't what he thinks it is."

Riley began to relay the message. "She said her name is Violet and…"

The remainder of her message was lost beneath Torcall's shouts. "Nay! Someone created this story and gave it to you, Riley. There is no one there. Don't believe her, Shaw. I refuse to listen to any more of this. You have all lost your minds. She cannot speak with the dead and neither can any of us." He sounded terrified, more than disbelieving. Riley barely recognized him as the strong, steady guard she'd learned to count on while she'd been here. He stalked away from the falls, finally calling back over his shoulder, "You've turned daft, Riley Cameron!"

CHAPTER EIGHT

R ILEY GASPED AT Torcall's outburst.
It was nothing she hadn't heard before.
Others had accused her of being daft, of making
up stories, and one person accused her of trying
to make money by selling her tales at festivals.

But she'd never expected it from Torcall.

She turned slowly back to the lovely woman
in front of her. "My apologies, but I don't think
Torcall wishes to hear what you have to say. I've
never seen him so upset."

"Nay, I have no' either. I belonged to Clan
Matheson in life. Shaw will know of me. But that
matters little. You must tell Torcall that he had
no hand in my death. It haunts him, keeps him
awake every night with guilt."

"I don't understand." She had no idea that
Torcall had the death of another lass on his
shoulders. She wished to ask the lass questions
about it, but then she would alert Shaw and Tara
to the ghost's words. She would not share that.

"He thinks the water he gave me killed me
because he retrieved it from the well when it
was poisoned. But he doesn't know that I was

already sickened. I'd already had enough of the poisoned water to end my life. I need to tell him it had naught to do with him. He thinks God will punish him for it, and God will not.

"Another lad, one who died shortly after I did, was the one who gave me a drink from the poisoned well. I loved him dearly, and we are together now for eternity, but I must break this tie holding me to the living world."

"What tie?"

"Torcall's guilt and misbelief about what happened. I must free him to be free myself. I did not tell Torcall I had a sweetheart, so he called on me and offered to help with my chores, including bringing water to my cottage. But I was sickened before he came, I just didn't show it yet. Torcall did not make me ill. It was Nils."

Riley didn't want to hear all she had to say. Had Torcall loved this woman?

"I can read your thoughts. I don't think he loved me, but he expressed an interest in me and said he would court me when I got over the curse. But I never got better. I died because of what I drank from Nils's bucket. Not Torcall's.

Riley turned to Shaw. "Did you know a lass named Violet?"

"Aye," Shaw said, clasping Tara's hand between both of his. "She died during the curse. Same as everyone else did, naught different. Torcall had some interest in her, but most people hadn't noticed it before she passed. What is she saying? Why did Torcall react so strongly?"

"Her message is for Torcall. Mayhap that

frightened him. Mayhap he really does no' believe I can speak with the dead." The implications of his outburst blossomed as she considered what he'd said. "If he thinks I'm daft, he won't wish to be near me." She cast a sad look at her sister, knowing her sister would understand exactly what she meant.

Tara was a wee bit too plain spoken. "Guess you'll no' find a relationship with a man who thinks you are daft."

Riley stared up at the gray skies, hoping to force the tear to stay in place and not land on her cheek. If she allowed one to fall, many would follow.

"You're right, Tara. There is no reason for me to stay." She spun on her heel and headed back to their horses. "I may as well go home now." But not until she gave Torcall the message from Violet.

From the one he loved.

No wonder Torcall hadn't expressed any interest in her. He was in love with another, one who would never come back. His very first love.

Tara called out to her. "You could at least hear what the ghost has to say. Then you can decide if you wish to give Torcall her message."

Riley faced Tara so her sister would see her eyes roll. Her hands settled on her hips. "That would be impossible."

Tara glanced over at Shaw, shrugging her shoulders at him. Shaw shook his head, seemingly equally puzzled. "Why?" she asked Riley.

"Because she's gone already. An absent ghost

cannot tell me anything." She had to catch Torcall and try to explain. She would not reveal Violet's comments to anyone but him until he gave her leave. She owed him that much.

When she reached the horses, his mount was already gone.

Torcall was nowhere to be seen.

If Violet was about to tell Riley how he'd killed her, he wasn't going to stand around to hear it. Mayhap he could convince Riley to keep his secret. He loved being part of Clan Matheson. He had no desire to live elsewhere at all.

He'd mounted in a hurry, joining the others on patrol. He didn't wish to be accused of leaving his post or shying from his duty. He said nothing about why he'd left the other three in the clearing.

Shaw, Tara, and Riley found them a few minutes later, and he led the group back to Eddirdale, their journey pleasant enough, if quiet. Once they arrived and the group scattered, Torcall led the three horses back to their stalls in the stable.

To his surprise, Riley followed him in, waving her sister on to the keep.

"When you are finished with your duties, I'd like to have a word with you, if you please."

Torcall's gut clenched, but he continued with his task, opening a stall door, leading the horse in, and pretending to brush the horse down. He couldn't look Riley in the eye.

"Go ahead. Say what you wish about Violet. But only between the two of us. 'Tis my only request." He kept his head down, hoping she'd tell him she knew the truth and then leave him be. If necessary, he would beg her not to reveal the truth to Marcas. He didn't wish to be banished from Clan Matheson.

Or judged by someone like Hairalt.

Riley stepped to where she could see him, though he wished she wouldn't. He nodded to her as if to tell her to continue.

Riley folded her hands in front of her, the act giving her the appearance of an angel, her blue riding outfit clinging to her curves in just the right places. His thoughts about her were hardly angelic, but he couldn't stop himself. She was beautiful, so pretty that he could think of nothing else.

"She said you didn't do it."

The brush clattered to the floor. He bent to retrieve it, going over her words in his mind, wondering how to answer without making himself look guilty. "Didn't do what exactly? And who is she?"

"Violet. She said you didn't bring her the drink from the well that sickened her. Nils visited her before you, and he brought her the tainted water first. She loved Nils but hadn't told you so."

He stepped closer, setting the brush on the shelf next to the stall. He had to make sure he understood everything correctly. "She said what?"

"She said that the man she loved, Nils, brought her the drink that made her sick. They shared a cup before you came to see her. She knows you feel guilty, but you needn't. It was Nils who gave her the poisoned drink."

"Nils?" He couldn't believe what she said, but how he wished it were true. He would force himself to believe it and stop dwelling on what he thought was true.

"Aye, Nils was sickened the same. They drank from the same goblet and died only a few hours apart. But she said she knew you felt guilty, and she must set you free of your guilt. It binds her to the living world, and she wished to continue on, where she can be with her love in complete freedom."

And just like that, his world changed.

Every day when he awakened, every night after he closed his eyes on his pallet, he thought of sweet Violet, how she might have lived if not for him, if he hadn't fetched the water for her from the poisoned well, the one he'd thought had better water than the stream behind her cottage. They'd learned the next day that the well was the cause of the illness in the clan. Marcas had said no one was to drink from the well or they'd be held accountable for their actions. Actions that could be counted as murder if intentional.

But now everything was different.

He wished to hug Riley for giving him this information, but he held back. If not for Shaw's tale of how Riley had helped reveal the truth of the MacKinnie clan's treachery, he might wonder if Riley could do what she claimed.

But this message proved her ability to speak

with those who'd passed on. No one else knew he gave that water to Violet.

It had to be Violet who told her.

The burden of guilt and regret, of wishing he could take back that water and pour it into the sea where it could harm no one, all those dark thoughts washed away from his mind, a cleansing rain shower washing it all from his shoulders. He turned away from Riley so she couldn't see the relief on his face, his head falling to rest on the horse's neck.

He prayed she would not see the tears that fell down his cheeks.

"Did you love her, Torcall?"

So many thoughts swirled through his mind that he barely heard Riley's question. By the time he turned around to answer her, she was gone.

CHAPTER NINE

TORCALL'S INABILITY TO answer was answer enough for Riley. He'd been in love with Violet. She hadn't returned the love, but that didn't mean it changed his feelings.

Some believed you only loved once in your life, that each person had a single soulmate and could never love another.

Did she wish to have Torcall's love if his true soulmate had passed on? Would he truly love her? She wished to be first in Torcall's mind.

Would being his second choice be enough?

She didn't know.

As she made her way toward the keep, a man ran toward her, a bouquet of winter greenery in his hand.

Hairalt.

She sighed, not ready to see him at the moment but unable to avoid him.

He stopped before her and performed a perfect bow before holding out the bouquet of fragrant pine, holly, and red berries in his hand. "For you, lovely lady."

Riley forced a smile for him and took the

flowers. "They are beautiful, Hairalt. Many thanks to you."

"Their beauty pales in comparison to yours. You are the most beautiful lass on Black Isle. Please say you'll allow me to take you to the winter festival on Milton land in two days."

Riley froze, unable to believe the man was being so persistent. "Hairalt, I am truly not interested in considering marriage at this time. I…"

"Marriage? I did no' mention such a thing. 'Twould only be the festival. I'll find you some pretty new ribbons."

He touched her hair, and she took a step back, uncomfortable.

"You're a nice lad, Hairalt, but…" She pulled away from his hand, a small voice echoing in her mind. *He touched you, he touched you…* She wished Torcall were there. He might not care for her the way she hoped for, but he had protected her at the festival.

"I'll not accept nay from you. I'll be here to escort you to the Milton festival at high sun the day after morrow."

And with that he was gone. She hadn't heard anything about a Milton festival. They would hear if outsiders were welcome.

She rubbed her hair where he'd touched her, wishing she could find a way to stop his forward behaviors. Men didn't just reach out and touch women wherever they wished. If her father were here, he would fix it for her. Hairalt was attractive and muscular, but something deceitful hid under his charming façade. Since their first interaction

at the Yule celebration, her instincts had told her
to beware of him, but whether it was merely a
woman's innate sense or her special abilities that
spoke to her, she couldn't say. Whatever his true
character might be, she was not interested in
learning more about Hairalt. Since her sire was
not available, he should be asking Marcas for
permission to court her. Why was he so boldly
ignoring conventions?

She had to admit she was far more interested
in Torcall Massie than Hairalt. It wouldn't bother
her if she never saw Hairalt again.

She continued toward the keep, and the
memory of his refusal to accept her answer about
the Milton festival had her hands tightening into
fists. She had to stop herself from tossing the
lovely bouquet. It wasn't the greens' fault that
Hairalt had chosen them.

Nonetheless, she was not interested in this
reminder of a man who took such liberties. If her
father had seen him touch her, the fool would
not dare to get so close to her again.

How she missed her parents. She made her
decision so quickly that she went directly to
her sister, not surprised to find her in the keep
chatting with Brigid and Jennet. Brigid sat in the
largest chair in the hall, perhaps the only one with
enough room for her burgeoning belly. She had
a cushion behind her back and her feet up on a
stool. Jennet stood next to the hearth, both hands
on her belly, and Tara stood behind her massaging
her shoulders.

"Jennet, are you ill?" Riley asked.

"Nay, I just have a knot in my neck, but your sister's fingers are magical," Jennet answered, her eyes closing and a soft murmur coming from her throat. "So magical."

Tara took one look at Riley and asked, "What's wrong? Did you speak with Torcall again?"

"Verra little. The lass at the glen was named Violet, and he knew her before she died from the curse. He'll no' tell me much else."

"Who gave you the bouquet?" Brigid asked. "There's a vase in the sideboard where the goblets are stored."

Tara fetched the vase and filled it with water, carefully arranging the holly for her sister while Riley sat down, gathering her thoughts before she shared them. She had to be certain before she made the announcement. Her sister would not be happy.

"Hairalt gave them to me."

"Oh, that was nice," Brigid said.

"Nay," Jennet retorted with a look of derision. "That lad always has an ulterior motive. I don't like him. He had a reason for giving you those greens, trust me."

"But he is handsome," Brigid pointed out.

"Doesn't make up for bad intentions." Riley flipped her braid back over her shoulder like a whip. She didn't like Hairalt, and after Torcall's reaction to her news about Violet in the stable, she had little chance with him. So be it. The three cousins all turned to stare at Riley, apparently waiting for her to elaborate.

"He invited me to go with him to the Milton festival in two days."

Jennet snorted and rolled her eyes. "I knew it. He's not to be trusted. He's got ulterior motives, I'm telling you."

Brigid looked at Tara. "Did he ask you for permission, Tara? He should since your parents are no' here. You are the only close relative able to vouch for her. He hasnae spoken to Marcas, either, as far as I know."

"Nay, he did no' ask me," Tara said. "Nor are you going with him, Riley. 'Twould be totally improper. I went to a festival with Shaw, but our sire watched our every move." She crossed her arms as if furious at Hairalt's boldness.

"Hardly," Riley said. "We did follow you there and checked on you, but you were left alone to sit near the loch with Shaw and without any chaperone at all." She knew her sister well enough to know almost everything that went through her mind. "Don't worry. I told him I would not attend with him."

Jennet snorted again. "And you think he would accept that?"

Jennet had an uncanny way of assessing people's inherent goodness. And badness. She apparently felt the same about Hairalt as Riley did. Jennet's impressions of the man confirmed that Riley's decision was the right one.

Riley fidgeted with a hangnail to avoid her sister's gaze. "You are correct, Jennet. He didn't accept my refusal. He said he would come for me, but that will be impossible because I won't be here." She rested her hands in her lap and lifted her chin, expecting arguments.

"Why not?" her sister asked. "You're no' wanting to leave because of him, are you? You should no' let him bully you into doing something you wouldn't do otherwise."

"I'm not being bullied. I miss Mama and Papa. You've all been pushing me and Torcall together, saying I should find a lad I like. And Hairalt says he wishes to spend time with me. I would ask Papa his opinion about all of them. He will have high standards for my husband, just as he did for yours. You were fortunate that he liked Shaw right away. But he'll tell me if Torcall is a worthy man. And if he didn't, Brin would. I miss him too." Her brother Brin was her greatest supporter during her spells, too. He was gentle in both his tone and his touch, which she desperately needed after having a vision of the future.

"Your mother is the smartest woman I know," Brigid said. "You can trust her, as well."

Jennet harrumphed and crossed her arms. "My mother is smarter than Aunt Jennie."

Brigid reached for her best friend's hand and gave it a squeeze. "They are both wonderful, but I think Aunt Jennie, being younger than your mother by quite a few years, might understand how Riley feels better than Aunt Brenna. And of course a mother knows her daughter better than anyone else could."

"Aye," Jennet said. "I cannot argue with that last point. You're serious about this, Riley? I hate to see you leave, but I know you miss them both."

"Aye, I am. I just wish to go home for a wee bit. Mayhap we'll be together during the holiday." Yule would be upon them soon, she realized with a start. How quickly the time had gone by.

"You must return when the bairns are born. Mine first." Brigid glanced down at her belly with such love that Riley could practically see it in the air around her. Jennet mirrored the same exact look, so much so that Riley wondered if she were seeing not Jennet but a lookalike. Jennet never revealed her emotions so clearly.

"How long do you suspect that will be, Brigid?" Riley asked. Everyone in the castle seemed to have different opinions of when the babes would arrive. She suspected the guards were making wagers on it.

Brigid chewed on her lip. "I think in about a moon."

"And you?" Riley asked Jennet.

"I'm not sure, but probably in about three moons."

"Two," said Brigid. "I cannot convince you that you are further along than you think."

Jennet shrugged and smiled. "When she's ready to come out, she will."

"A lass, you think?" Tara asked.

"Aye, but Brigid's having a lad," Jennet replied.

"Whatever you have, they will both be a blessing." Riley turned to her sister. "I'm going to plan on leaving at dawn the day after the morrow. Tara, will you ask Shaw to arrange it for me?"

"Of course. I'll take care of everything. You

look exhausted. Go rest until supper. You'll feel better."

Riley nodded and headed up the stairs. As she turned toward her chamber, she just managed to overhear Brigid say, "I must go speak with Marcas."

Was it about Hairalt? It didn't matter. She just wished to go home where she was safe and loved and didn't have to see Torcall or Hairalt every day and decide what to do about them.

Life was getting too difficult.

CHAPTER TEN

T ORCALL STOOD OUTSIDE the stables at dawn the day Riley was leaving, brushing his horse down and filling a sack with oats for the day-and-a-half-long trip.

He'd been surprised when Shaw came to him the previous morn and told him Riley was going home. Disappointment flooded through him, but he didn't want Shaw to see how important Riley had become to him, so he kept his feelings to himself.

"With so little warning? Is Tara going with her?"

"Hellfire, nay. Tara belongs on Matheson land with me. I'm sending you along to protect my wife's sister." Shaw gave him a serious look that said he would not allow Torcall to refuse this order.

Torcall had nodded his acceptance, though he couldn't say if he was glad of the assignment or dreading it.

He'd hoped to speak with Riley, but she'd spent her day packing and resting for the journey, never setting foot outside the keep. Now he was awaiting her, and he had butterflies roiling around in his belly unlike he'd ever had before.

He knew why. He didn't want Riley to leave. He had more to say to her, and he'd run out of time. More than anything, he wished to get to know her better. This journey was his last chance, until she returned for another visit with her sister, and God knew when that might be. He'd speak to her as soon as she arrived. It was high time to tell her exactly how he felt. Perhaps she could forestall her journey a few days.

The sound of laughter caught his attention, and he spun around. Riley crossed the courtyard toward him with Tara, Jennet, and Brigid surrounding her. Someone must have said something funny, and he wished he could listen to the lilt of her laughter all day long. Preferably when *he'd* said something to cause it.

Hairalt came barreling down the path from outside the curtain wall, a bouquet of dried flowers in his hand. The bastard approached the group of ladies without an invitation, breaking into their small gathering.

"For you, fairest Riley. I will follow you to the to the ends of the earth if you do not promise to return to attend the next festival with me."

He bowed gallantly, and Riley started, glancing at her sister. But it was Jennet who spoke, surprising everyone.

"Give me that ill-intended bunch of flowers." She tossed them off to the side and stomped on them. "Stop trying to bend her will to your way by giving her gifts. She'll not return here for you, Hairalt. Be gone."

Hairalt stared at her, clearly shocked, and Torcall had to stifle a grin. Riley opened her mouth to speak, but Tara set her hand on her sister's forearm. "Forgive her rudeness. I'll say it quietly. My sister has no interest in your attentions. Please leave us so we can enjoy our parting without interruption. She has stated her refusal to accompany you clearly. If you truly had high regard for her, you would abide by her preferences. I am appalled that you invited her to go to a festival with you without proper escort."

Hairalt stepped back and crossed his arms. "Her parents are not here. What proper escort could she have?"

"Me! My husband and I would chaperone the two of you. Or Jennet and Ethan. The Matheson laird takes the safety of his guests seriously, as does his family. No man so inconsiderate of a lady's reputation is worthy of her company. Please take your leave now."

Hairalt scowled, but the expression disappeared as quickly as it had come. A quick moment and his charming façade returned. "Forgive me, my ladies. I've heard the road between Black Isle and Cameron land is difficult. Surely you would not object to an additional guard."

Tara said, "My husband chose the guards, and you are no' one of them, Hairalt. Leave."

He nodded to Riley, then hurried toward the stable. He shot Torcall a glare as he went by, as if the ladies' dismissal were his fault.

Torcall's earlier ambivalence evaporated. He was now very glad Shaw had given him this assignment. Alvery and two other new guards were going along; the four of them would get her safely to Cameron land. At the last minute, an older woman came out to join them.

Tara looked at her sister and shrugged. "I cannot go with you, so I feel you should have another female. Alvery's wife Una agreed to travel with you."

As one of the stable lads brought Riley's horse out of the stable, Shaw, a bedroll and pack slung across his back, joined the ladies with a grin. "I think it's best if I go along as well."

"I did not know you were going, husband," Tara said, "but I'm glad you are. I'd join you if my two cousins weren't so close to their times."

Shaw wrapped his arms around his wife and kissed her hard on the lips. "I'd like to tell you that it was completely out of the goodness of my heart, but I fear your father will have my arse cleaved in two if I do not protect your sister personally."

Tara gave him a big smile and hugged him. "I cannot argue your reasoning. Godspeed. I'll be watching for you. Take good care of my only sister."

They mounted their horses, Torcall, Alvery, his wife, and the two new guards, brothers Dagr and Egill. Shaw helped Riley onto her white mare while the stable lad loaded the last of their baggage onto the pack horse.

Just as they turned for the gate, Hairalt led his

horse out of the stable, mounted and rode to join them. "I'm coming along."

Torcall bit back his fury and managed to keep his voice level when he said, "Nay, Hairalt. You'll be staying back."

"I don't take orders from you, Massie, and I wish to come. Riley, I've heard you often have your spells while riding. I wish to observe you, strictly to learn how I could help you in the future." He was the picture of innocence, but Torcall wished for nothing more than to wipe that expression off Hairalt's face with his fist. "I promise to keep watch over you, so someone will be close by when you have your next spell."

Riley didn't even turn her head to look at Hairalt, but Torcall could read her displeasure clear as day. Even Ethan, just riding in from a patrol, seemed to sense that something was amiss. He directed his horse toward their little cluster of riders.

"She's not some oddity to observe," Torcall said. "She's a lass who has special skills that she wishes to keep private. Dismount. If you follow, you'll have to deal with me."

"Do something, Shaw," Tara said. "He's naught but trouble. I already plan to speak with Marcas about banning him from the clan."

"We need no' be that severe yet," Shaw said. He positioned his horse to block Hairalt's way. "I'm ordering you to stay back. Massie has been given express authority to command the new guards, including you, and I stand behind his order for you to dismount and tend to your duties here.

We have enough men, and we don't need a man along who will not take orders."

"Why not ask the lady? I'm sure Riley would love to have me along, and I know the Mathesons take pride in pleasing their women." Hairalt ran his hand through his carefully combed short blond locks, putting every stray hair back in place, then set his hand on his hip and looked to Riley for her response.

Riley's face turned red. She hated being the center of attention, so Torcall spoke for her. "Riley would say nay."

Riley nodded but did not make eye contact with either Torcall or the boorish Hairalt. "I do say nay. If you wish to please me, Hairalt, you will stay here."

Ethan pulled up next to Shaw and said, "Hairalt, you're needed here. Shaw, take your leave. I'll see that he stays back."

Torcall nodded to Ethan and moved his horse abreast of Riley. "Come, my lady. 'Tis time to take our leave."

"Torcall will ride lead on this journey," Shaw said. "I'll take the back. Move along."

Riley glanced over at Torcall, relief on her face. "Many thanks to you, Torcall."

His heart skipped a beat. "'Twas my pleasure, my lady."

They made camp just before dark, ate the smoked salmon and rolls studded with currants that Jinny had prepared for them, then roasted apples in the fire. In a small clearing off the main track, Torcall and Shaw put a tarp over a tree limb and staked it out enough for Riley and Una to sleep underneath.

Riley said, "'Tis a cold night. I'm glad for the protection. My thanks to ye."

Torcall said, "Even we have a thin one in the winter. One never knows when a storm cloud could come upon us. You'll be warmer. I'll sleep in front of the tent and Shaw behind you while the others will sleep on either side. 'Tis an important part of our protection of you."

"I don't think I need that much guarding. 'Tis night. Who would come along in the winter?"

"'Tis for your safety, Riley. And our own. I do no' wager I'd live a long and healthy life if your sire learned we did no' guard you well."

Torcall settled in for the night after making sure Riley was comfortable. He stared up at the stars, wondering how he could speak to her as they traveled. Once they arrived on Cameron land, it would be even more difficult to find time alone with her.

He closed his eyes with the same thought he'd had so often over the last few weeks. Mayhap on the morrow…

Torcall slept restlessly, his rest troubled by visions of Riley running through a glen, a man chasing her. When he got close enough, the man looked like Hairalt, but then he would change, his eyes becoming those of a serpent.

"Hairalt, leave her be!"

But it wasn't Hairalt. The monster threw his head back gleefully. "You'll never see her again." The monster that was—and wasn't—Hairalt snatched Riley up and disappeared into thin air.

Torcall woke with a start, his skin clammy from the nightmare. He sat up and listened, heard naught but an owl. He peeked inside the makeshift tent to make sure Riley was all right, but she wasn't there. His heart raced.

He scrambled up and headed toward the burn, relieved to see her sitting on a large rock in the light of the moon. He didn't wish to frighten her, but he had to see if she was well.

"Riley, did something wake you?"

She looked over her shoulder. "Nay, naught. I couldn't sleep."

"May I sit?" he asked, the boulder clearly large enough for both of them.

"You'd be most welcome." She patted the stone beside her. "Hairalt is haunting my thoughts. I have this fear that he's followed me and will pop out from behind a tree."

"You have five strong guards to protect you. I'd never allow him to hurt you." He locked gazes with her, and after a long, silent moment, she turned her head away. They both faced the burn. She had a leaf in her lap she was quietly tearing to shreds.

"My thanks to you, Torcall. I think there's something evil about him, and evil men can find a way around other men. And they have no honor in a fight. I don't want him anywhere near me. I don't understand why he has continued to pursue me. After the first night we met, I've done naught to encourage him." She stared at the leaf bits in her lap and brushed them away.

"I can answer that. 'Tis simple. You are beautiful, Riley, more so than any lass in either Clan Milton or Clan Matheson. Many would love to court you, but they fear your father or your special skills."

"I don't believe that, Torcall. I see no reason why anyone would be afraid to court me."

This was his chance. "Well, I would like to court you, but I'm afraid you'll reject me. You are the daughter of a chieftain, and I'm merely a guard, with no standing whatsoever." He took her hand, cocooning it in his against the chill of the night. "I think about you all the time, but I'll not pursue you until I have your sire's permission. He may wish for a chieftain's son for you." He could barely speak his fear without flinching, but now that he'd confessed his feelings, he felt a weight lift from his heart.

"Torcall, my sire considers a guard's job to be one of the finest. He will welcome you, I'm sure of it, especially since Marcas and his brothers hold you in such high regard." Happiness lit up her eyes, and he caught his breath to see it. He wanted to get closer.

"My lady Riley, would it be too forward of me to ask you the favor of a kiss?"

"Forward or no', I'd be very happy to grant you that favor." Her lips twitched with a nervous smile.

He leaned forward, pausing just a moment before placing his lips against hers. It was a chaste kiss, but he would treasure the feeling of her warm lips against his as sweet as anything he'd ever experienced. He pulled back after only a breath.

"Thank you, my lady."

She cupped his cheeks in her palms. "'Twas my pleasure, sir. And that kiss was definitely not forward. *This* is being forward." She leaned toward him, her lips settling against his with a force that took him by surprise, but he matched her quickly enough, her desire for him making him bold. He touched his tongue to the seam of her lips, and she parted for him, allowing him a taste of her. If he never kissed her again, the memory of it would last him a lifetime. She angled her mouth against his, and their tongues dueled in a light dance. She wasn't experienced, he could tell, but she also wanted more.

He ended the kiss before he lost his self-control. "I'll no' do anything more until I speak with your sire."

Riley sighed happily. "Naught would please me more, Torcall. Please do no' wait long."

Then she hopped off the rock, winked, and walked back toward their campsite with a saucy wiggle of her hips. His mouth went dry.

He had definitely fallen for Riley Cameron.

CHAPTER ELEVEN

~~~

THEY ARRIVED ON Cameron land just before supper. Riley's heart was still singing at Torcall's declaration that he would request permission to court her when they arrived, and riding through the gates of Cameron castle only multiplied her happiness.

Her father was the first out the door of the keep, and she jumped off her horse and hurried to give him a swift hug. Then her mother's still-nimble feet flew across the cobblestones toward her, and they embraced as well.

"Riley, I'm so pleased to see you. Welcome home, my sweet. And under such wonderful circumstances. Someone is asking for your hand, and he is charming!" Her mother kissed her cheek, then stepped back, grasping her hands with a wide smile on her face. Her voice dropped to a whisper. "And he's so handsome too."

Riley glanced over her shoulder, finding Torcall settling their horses and chatting with the stable master.

Her mother had come from the opposite direction—the keep. Riley's belly churned.

"Who asked for my hand, Mama?"

Her mother gave her father a puzzled look. "Why, Hairalt. He's such a nice man. He told me he proposed to you and you accepted. I was surprised you would agree to marry before he spoke to your sire. But Tara is capable of giving you good advice and assessing any possible husband for you."

Riley's blood boiled with fury, but she held in the unladylike curse. She had to stay calm while she explained the truth of the situation to her parents. "Hairalt is no' my betrothed. I do no' like him at all, though he won't hear it when I tell him so. He wanted to come along as a guard, and Torcall, Shaw, and Ethan all had to tell him no. He has no respect for orders from his laird, clearly. He must have snuck away and ridden like the wind to arrive ahead of us. I will not marry Hairalt. Never. And you can tell him that I said so."

Before they could continue their conversation, the courtyard burst into activity. Riley's brother Brin called out to her father from the stables, so the older man headed to join him. Torcall was busy trying to calm one of their horses. And many of the castle residents hurried into the courtyard to greet Riley. It felt so good to be surrounded by the love of her clanmates, and she clasped arms and embraced as many of them as she could reach.

She was so absorbed in the welcoming crowd that she was caught off guard when an arm snaked around her waist and tugged her against a hard male body. Thoughts of Torcall disappeared as soon as she glanced over her shoulder to see the handsome grin she was beginning to hate so much. Hairalt had pulled her close enough to kiss.

She jerked against his hold but could not get free.

"Riley, will you no' introduce me to your clanmates? They should know the man you're going to marry, don't you think? I know you're looking forward to our wedding before the next full moon."

He flashed a wide grin, and many of the lasses around them giggled in awkward admiration.

"Take your hand from the lass." Torcall broke through the crowd, his hand already on the hilt of his sword.

Hairalt snorted, but he did not let Riley go, even when she tried to pull away. "Riley makes that decision, not you." Then he turned away and tried to give Riley a kiss on her cheek, but she ducked, and she hoped he got a mouthful of hair.

"Hairalt, we are *no'* betrothed. Let me go!"

He leaned in to whisper to her. "But we will be. You'll see. No one rejects me, Riley."

He straightened and seemed to be about to taunt Torcall. But the other man cracked his fist into Hairalt's jaw so hard that he reeled back. Torcall caught Riley to him, keeping Hairalt from pulling her along with him as he stumbled.

"If she marries anyone, 'twill be me, no' you, Hairalt," Torcall declared.

And while Riley was grateful for Torcall's assistance, she wished he would not try to make her decisions for her. "I thank you, Torcall, but my marriage will be my choice." And she stepped away from him.

The group became quiet at Riley's words.

Torcall calmed immediately. "Forgive me. I should no' have made any declaration. 'Twas wrong of me. Please forgive me."

She could feel her face heating at all the attention, and she wished everyone would just go away now. Her father came up behind Torcall, Brin next to him.

"What's happened here? Did someone hurt my daughter?" He looked from Riley to his wife, but Riley pushed through the crowd and headed toward the keep.

"Riley!" her sire called, but she had to get out of everyone's sight. She raced inside and headed up the staircase to her chamber, falling face first onto the fresh linen and soft pillows, kept clean and ready for her return.

She caught her breath then rolled to her back and looked around the beloved space. The different colors in her chamber made it look springlike, even in darkest winter. A white coverlet adorned her bed, but she had pillows of light blue, pink, light green, yellow, and a wonderful lavender. Dried flowers hung from the rafters and sat in a vase on the mantle. Her chest of drawers was decorated with a finely embroidered linen runner across its surface.

The tears came slowly, but she didn't try to stop them, instead taking the time to look at all the little treasures around the room, most of them made by her dear mother. How she adored her home and family.

A knock sounded at her door, and she wished it could be Tara. But it had to be her mother, her father, or Brin.

"Come in."

Her mother came in and sat on the side of the bed, stroking Riley's cheek as only her mother could. "Too much attention instead or not enough?"

Her mother also had the knack of expressing a problem in fewer than ten words. "Aye, that and Hairalt. He will no' leave me alone, and I hate him more every time I see him. He was no' supposed to come, yet here he is, defying his laird's orders. Marcas told him he was forbidden. So just the fact that he was here upset me, and I took my temper out on Torcall. I should no' have. He is the one I trust, the one who I hope to spend more time with."

"Why did they tell Hairalt not to come? He is a Matheson guard, is he no'?

"He is, Mama, as a trial. He just asked to join the clan recently. He's presumptuous, always telling me what I'm going to do. He hears nothing I say, and I don't think he cares for anyone but himself. I don't like him. Or his kisses."

Her mother arched a brow. "My wee lassie is growing up, I see." Riley smiled at her mother, who patted her leg in reassurance. "So we will reject Hairalt's request, but what about Torcall? We've met him before, and he's a fine guard and a fine man."

She sighed, then pushed herself to a sitting position next to her mother. "I do like Torcall, but I didn't wish for him to tell everyone. He's supposed to ask Papa for permission to court me first, then ask if he can have my hand, then ask me. Is that no' how 'tis supposed to go?"

"Aye, and I was put off by Hairalt's tale that you'd already accepted his suit. It didn't seem like you to do so. When I left the chaos, Torcall was talking with your sire. I suspect he could be asking for permission to court you. What answer should your father give him? Aye or nay?"

"Aye. I would like to get to know him better. But why did he have to say that in front of everyone? Now I'll have to answer everyone's questions. *When will the wedding be? Here or on Black Isle? How many bairns will you have?* You know how it goes."

"We'll quash the questions. Will that please you?"

"Aye, if you can. What's done is done. But why must men think a lass has no mind? Do they no' know we can make our own decisions?" She played with her fingernails, debating what to say to Torcall when she saw him.

"I'm sure Torcall respects your ability to make decisions. He just has that male way of wanting to protect your honor. It makes men do silly things, but I still believe 'tis a good thing to have as part of one's character. Obviously, Hairalt does no' have any wee bit of that trait in his personality. I also think Torcall was reacting as much to you as he was to Hairalt. His eyes were on you, and you were clearly upset with Hairalt."

"You noticed that?" She looked up at her mother, hopeful that she wasn't completely wrong about Torcall, that he did respect her and knew she could make her own decisions. Her papa often spoke of that same trait in men, so her mother wasn't wrong.

"Aye, I did, so do no' be too hard on the man. Why do you no' come down for supper and have a chat with your brother and your sire? They missed you."

"All right. My thanks to you, Mama."

"I think you have another reason to like Torcall." Her mother smiled and smoothed Riley's hair before they stepped into the passageway.

"What reason is that?"

"He knows of your special talents, and he accepts them. True?"

"Aye, he does."

"And has Hairalt seen you have a spell?"

She nodded. "Aye, once, but I'm no' sure he paid me much attention then. I had one on my horse and he was along on the trip. He may have seen it or no'. But now he wishes to *observe* me. I find his request creepy."

"He wants to watch you, as if you are something unique?"

"Watch in a strange way. You know the type."

Her mother opened the door and said, "I surely do. I'll keep an eye on that man from now on."

Riley moved to the top of the steps and looked at Torcall in the hall below. He was seated at the guards' table, but as soon as his gaze fell on her, he got up and moved to the bottom of the staircase.

So did Hairalt.

Her sire rose from his seat at the head table. "Hairalt, I'll have a word with you outside."

"I'll go with you, Laird," Shaw said, also rising. "He has to answer to me."

Perhaps she'd never see Hairalt again. Could she be that lucky?

She suspected he would not give up so easily.

CHAPTER TWELVE

S HAW AND THE other Matheson guards left the next morning, but he ordered Torcall to stay. "I've no doubt of Cameron's ability to protect Riley, but Hairalt was a Matheson guard, so our clan bears some responsibility. Hairalt will be back, I do not doubt. I charge you with protecting Riley and ending the threat he poses."

"I'll protect her with my life, Shaw."

"I know you will. I'll inform Marcas of Hairalt's behavior and make sure that he is no longer a member of Clan Matheson."

"I'll ride out with you, then do a search on my way back here and look for any evidence of the bastard. 'Twould be good to know which way he went."

He escorted Shaw's group to the boundary of Cameron land, then began his patrol. He knew Cameron land well from other visits here, and he followed the patrol route he knew the Cameron guards used. A group of travelers wearing red Grant plaids approached on a different path than the one Shaw had left on.

Torcall hailed them—a man, a woman, and

a young lass and a contingent of guards—and they pulled their horses to a stop. The woman's hair was nearly white, and she made a striking impression as she sat on her black horse.

"Connor Grant!" Torcall called. "'Tis good to see you again."

"Well met, Torcall Massie. What brings you here from Black Isle? No trouble, I hope."

"Nay, not if I have any say in it. I am here to protect Riley, who just returned from a stay with the Matheson clan."

Connor nodded. "She could not have a better guard. This is my wife Sela and our daughter Dyna."

"Greetings to you all. I'm headed back to the castle, so I'll travel along with you if you don't mind."

Connor nodded, so Torcall fell in next to Dyna. "You ride well for a young lass," he said.

"I'm a better rider than all three of my cousins, who are lads. Do you think lasses are no' skilled?" She locked gazes with him, her look too knowing by far for such a young girl.

"Nay, I know lasses and lads can all be good at lots of things." He didn't say any more, looking away.

"Which lasses are the smartest?"

"Dyna, we shall no' offend the guard we just met, please," her mother said.

"I do no' mind answering," Torcall said with a smile. "Lady Cameron and her two daughters are very bright. The mistress of Clan Matheson, Brigid, is also verra intelligent, as is her cousin

Jennet. She is probably the most intelligent person I've ever met, lad or lass."

"Fair enough," she muttered. "Sorry, Mama."

"How many years have you?"

"Nearly ten." He'd overestimated by a couple years, not that she looked that much older, but she *sounded* that mature.

Connor asked, "And how do my cousins fare? Did I no' hear that Brigid is carrying her first babe?"

"Aye, as is Jennet, though Brigid is farther along than her cousin."

"How many more moons for Brigid?" Sela asked.

"Only one. She looks fit to burst."

"Uncle Logan and Aunt Gwyneth will be there soon. He won't leave until that bairn is born, is my guess."

They arrived at the gate to shouts of surprise. Brin was the first to greet them. "Connor, is that you?"

"Aye, it is. Thought we'd come by for a visit."

"What brings you?" Brin asked. "I'm mighty glad to see you. I'll take any time you're willing to give me to work on my sword skills." Connor was noted as one of the best swordsmen in all the land, after his sire and his uncle Loki.

"Dyna had a sudden urge to visit Riley and Aunt Jennie. We never argue with her odd senses."

Torcall looked at Dyna again and raised his eyebrows.

She looked right back and said, "I'll be talking to you later. We have something to discuss."

Her eyes narrowed, and a chill traveled up his spine. He didn't answer, just went about the chore of stabling his horse. The rest all stayed in the courtyard, sharing greetings with the Camerons. He brushed his horse, got him a flake of hay, then took a moment to lean on the stall door and give the beast a final pat.

"You're a seer."

Torcall nearly jumped out of his skin. He spun to see Dyna standing between him and the stable door. "What? I'm no seer, lass."

"Aye, you are. Pay attention to your dreams. Then you'll understand. You cannot fight the talents you are given." She spun on her heel and ran out of the stable.

He didn't know what to make of either her declaration or her instructions. Pay attention to his dreams? The only one that came to him was the dream about the monster stealing Riley away. The serpent that had originally looked like Hairalt.

The hairs on the back of his neck rose. He knew the bastard would return, and he would not leave Riley unguarded until the danger was gone. Torcall joined the group heading to the keep for the midday meal, then stopped when he realized Aedan Cameron was behind him.

He turned around and said, "My lord, may I have a moment of your time?"

His boldness surprised even himself. If he'd taken the time to think on what he was about to do, he would not have had the courage.

"Aye, follow me to my solar."

He nodded, going over exactly what he wished to say to this man whom he admired so much, the man who had raised two bright, talented daughters. One of whom he was about to fall in love with, if he hadn't already.

No. Truth was, he already loved Riley.

Aedan opened the door and gestured toward a chair facing the desk while he sat behind it. "You wished to speak with me, Torcall?"

Torcall sat, leaned back in his chair, and thought about exactly what he wished to say. "I've grown verra fond of your daughter, and I would like your permission to court her. She's verra bright and has a kind heart. If you've no' chosen a man for her, I would like the chance to get to know her better, then to offer for her if we suit." He knew he had to be completely upfront with Aedan Cameron, so he went on. "I'm not a nobleman, but I've worked as a guard for the Mathesons since I turned five and ten, I've remained loyal to my laird, and I'm sure he would vouch for my character."

"Nay, no need, Torcall. I know you to be an honorable man, and I care not about noble blood. In my eyes, our blood is the same. Ask my wife, and she'll tell you 'tis true. A nobleman doesn't bleed any differently than you do. But tell me. How do you feel about Riley's special skills? Can you love a wife who has such a calling? It would require you to stay close to her or have another with her at all times, especially when a fall or other harm might come to her, on horseback or at the edge of the sea, for example."

"I've been with her on at least two occasions when she's had one of her spells, and I'm grateful I've been able to assist her. 'Tis far more difficult for her than for me. I accept her as she is; these abilities have made her who she is, a remarkable and caring woman." Thinking about what Dyna had just told him, he continued, "I consider it something special, a gift from the angels for Riley to have the ability to help souls complete their journey home."

"A gift. Hmmm…" Aedan sat back in his chair and crossed his arms. "I've never thought of it in such a way. So my answer would be that anyone who considers my daughter's special skills a gift should be given the chance to court her. I believe Riley will welcome your suit. She told her mother as much last eve, in fact. And I'd much rather have you courting her than that bastard Hairalt. I have already banned him from our land and made sure all my men know exactly what he looks like. If he has half a brain, he'll not return to cause any more trouble."

"I made a search for him this morning but didn't find a hint of where he might have gone. I suspect he's simply biding his time."

"No matter for this issue. I'm pleased to grant you permission to court my daughter, and"—he stood up and held his hand out, giving Torcall's a hard shake when he clasped it—"she'll be verra happy when she hears this news. Go and find the lass and let her know. If you wish to take another patrol later, go south. There are many hidey holes t hat direction where a sneaking, plotting bastard might hope to go unnoticed."

Torcall gave the laird a bow and took his leave, pleased to have gotten the permission he had hoped for. Now if he could just get over the nervousness he felt every time he was near Riley.

But even more importantly, how could he win Riley's love in return?

CHAPTER THIRTEEN

RILEY SAW TORCALL and her father go into
the solar, and her sire winked at her as they
entered. Not wishing to be inside the keep when
they finished their conversation, she hurried
outside, surprised to see a lovely blue sky and an
oddly warm sun for winter. She'd just reached
the curtain wall when she felt a spell coming on.
She leaned against one of the supporting walls
and closed her eyes.

Instantly, she was back in the faerie glen on
Black Isle. She knew she hadn't been bodily
transported there, but it felt as real as if she had.

Violet stepped out of the forest toward her.
"Riley, we need your help! It's difficult to speak
to you this way, so you must listen carefully."

"Why is it difficult?"

"Because you are far from the faerie glen and
evil swirls around you, blocking our message.
Listen! Speak to Torcall about his dreams. He
does not realize that he dreams true, and so he
pays his dreams no mind and often cannot recall
them. We've tried to send him warnings, but

because he does not know their nature, he does not understand they're meant to help you."

"Warnings about what?"

"Torcall will uncover the truth of the evil spirit, but he won't understand it until he accepts his purpose. Tell him to pay attention to his dreams. We'll guide you both through them. It takes only one voice to defy the spirits and upset them. Don't be that voice, Riley. Be strong…"

Then Violet was gone, fading away mid-sentence.

"What the hell did that mean?" Riley shouted into the glen, but of course, there was no answer.

She blinked and found herself still leaning against the strong wall of Cameron Castle, and no one seemed to have noticed her. A few people worked in the courtyard, but they kept to their own work. Sometimes she wondered how others could be so oblivious to the spirits and the shimmering in the air that came with her spells.

She took a deep breath and pushed off the wall. A walk would help her recover from the vision, she knew, and she started across the courtyard toward the gate. She could see Lochluin Abbey in the distance, a comforting presence all her life. With her eyes fixed on the abbey steeple, she nearly ran into her uncle Ruari.

"Riley, are you well?" He grabbed her by the shoulders and looked straight into her eyes.

"I'm fine, Uncle Ruari. I just need to move about. I thought I'd…" She thought quickly. "Take a ride to the abbey and visit the monks." Thrilled that she'd thought of something, she turned her feet toward the stable, her uncle at her side.

"Please allow me to escort you. You should not ride out alone." Uncle Ruari didn't wait for an answer, instead calling for two horses from the stable lad.

"Oh, are you going to the abbey?" Brin asked as he came up beside their uncle. "I'd like to come too. I haven't had much chance to speak with you, sister."

She nodded, too exhausted from the spell to argue. When a third horse was ready, the three of them mounted, and she let the two men lead the way out. She managed to stay upright until they arrived at the abbey.

Brin dismounted and said, "Uncle, you can return if you like. I'll take Riley inside to meet the new monks and see her home."

Uncle Ruari nodded and took his leave.

Riley stayed in her saddle, rethinking her plan. "New monks? I'm not sure I'm ready for that."

"Aye. If you don't wish you to meet them, you don't have to. I know you had a spell. I can always tell when you are coming out of one. Do you wish to talk about it?"

Riley loved how her brother asked what she wanted, after her spell, compared to Tara's demanding to know what she'd seen. And normally, she would talk to Brin about the vision. But this time, she shook her head. She wasn't ready.

"Nay. I mean, I did have a small one, but I'm

fine now. Tell me more about the new monks. How many?"

"Two, I believe. One is named Bate, short for Bartholomew. The other I don't recall. But Bate is very friendly. Do you wish to meet him?" Brin helped her down from her horse and offered her his arm, as he always knew to do after a spell. He led her toward the abbey wall. "I hope you were someplace safe when the spell came on."

All the lasses adored her brother because he was tall, handsome, and gentle. Dark hair fell across one eye, and he smiled easily, melting hearts wherever he turned. Riley loved his gentleness the best, but he was persistent, too, especially when it came to ensuring her well-being.

"Inside the curtain wall, so safe enough. I leaned against it, and when I woke up, it seemed as if naught had happened."

"I should have kept you home, but since I noticed Torcall and Da go off together, I have a feeling I know why you wished to be away from there right now."

She gave her brother a knowing look and squeezed his arm. He always knew.

They strolled around the outside of the abbey and into the gardens in the rear. There wasn't much growing at this time of year, but there were a few men cutting greens for the holiday and cleaning up branches dropped from the wind. The monks were meticulous with the grounds of the abbey.

Two men stopped and waved to them. Hob,

one of her favorite monks, set down his tools and joined her and Brin.

"Greetings to you, my lady Riley. Come meet our newest member Brother Bate." He called out to a man cutting down hanging tree branches.

Bate nodded to her and gave her a wide smile. He was younger and more handsome than she had expected.

"'Tis my pleasure to meet you, Brother," she said, nodding.

"'Tis my honor, my lady. I've heard much about you already."

"Brother Hob!" someone called out from the back entrance to the abbey. "Would you lead Brin to the abbot's office, please? He has a message for his sire."

"Aye, we'll be right there. Brother, keep Riley entertained, would you please?"

"Why don't you join me on the bench over there? I was about to take a rest anyway." Bate gestured to a corner of the garden as Hob and Brin disappeared into the building.

"That would be lovely." She followed him to the bench and took a seat in the sun.

"Are you too cold, my lady? We could go inside."

"Nay, I'm fine. My mantle has a double thickness thanks to my talented mother. Tell me how you ended up here."

He shrugged, and she had the intense urge to brush the one lock that repeatedly fell from the side on his face. While he had the standard monk haircut, the wind always blew stray hairs about.

Bate had the greenest eyes she'd ever seen. Even greener than her sire's and her brother's eyes. She was strangely drawn to him, and wanted to move closer, touch his cheek. She found herself staring at his lips, wondering what a monk would taste like.

"Lady Riley?"

She blushed when she realized she hadn't been listening well. "Excuse me? What did you say?"

"I said that I'm only here for a short time. I travel to Europe in a matter of days. If I am judged a good representative, I hope to join a delegation to meet the Pope."

Someone called her name from the front of the abbey, and she turned to see Torcall approaching, a basket over his arm. "I thought we could have lunch together in the greenhouse. I was told we are welcome there. Would you care to join me?"

With one look at Torcall, his light hair curling against his collar, the strength in his arms, and the sword at his side, all fascination with Bate evaporated. This was the man she might marry. He was the one she wanted to kiss, not some monk fresh out of his devotions and dedicated to God.

"I would love to join you, Torcall, and I am hungry. May we find a place not far? I'm not interested in going back inside just yet. 'Tis too beautiful out not to enjoy this sunny day. We don't get many sunny days with blue skies in winter." True, it was cold, but no snow had fallen yet and the sun felt good on her face and shoulders. Many people were out of doors, taking advantage and enjoying the day, and she wanted to do the same.

She stood and nodded to the monk. "It was lovely to meet you, Brother. I would like to hear more about your path when I return another day."

"'Twill be my pleasure to speak to you any time, my lady." Bate gave her a warm smile, then returned to his work in the garden, waving as he left.

Torcall held his hand out to her and said, "I noticed a table in the front of the abbey that sits in the sun. I think it would be warmer there than here. I brought a plaid for you to sit on so you won't be cold."

"Wonderful. I'll follow you wherever you go, Torcall." She knew of that table. Uncle Ruari had suggested it because there were often many visitors to the abbey, especially in the summer. Her uncle was assigned protection of the abbey and he took his charge very seriously. And that included making everyone happy too.

She smiled up at Torcall and chastised herself for thinking for even a moment that Bate was good looking. Torcall was far better looking in every way. And besides, monks did not marry or carry on—they were married to the church.

They reached the table, and Torcall set the basket down, pulling a plaid off the top and spreading it across the bench.

"Your throne, my lady."

She laughed and sat. "You surprise me, Torcall. I wasn't expecting this at all."

He sat down next to her. "Well, I wanted to give

you the news. I asked your father for permission to court you."

"I was hoping that was why you two went off to his solar this morning." She wouldn't tell him what this step meant to her—that she was desirable and could hope for a future with him. That he hadn't dismissed her because she was different. "What did he say?"

Undoubtedly, everyone in Cameron Castle knew that Torcall had met with her father and probably had surmised why. But she hoped she would be the first to hear her father's answer.

"He gave me his support. He said my blood was the same as a nobleman's, that he cared more that a man was honorable than who his father was."

"Silly. I told you he would no' care that you're a guard. He's said it many times—everyone's blood looks the same when you bleed from a cut. I'm glad, Torcall." She smiled and took the oatcake he offered her, breaking off a piece to chew.

He sat down next to her. "I am too. Your sire is a fine man, and if I were no' sworn to Marcas, I'd be proud to serve him."

"Did he ask you any questions?" She wanted every detail of their conversation.

"Aye, he asked me how I felt about your special skill. And I said I did not care, that I would always take care of you. 'Tis part of why I love you, Riley." His hand came up and cupped her cheek, and he leaned forward, gazing into her eyes.

Her belly did flips at having him this close to her. Then his lips settled on hers, and he kissed her, lightly at first, but with a passion that told her he wanted to be with her. He angled his head so he could deepen the kiss, take more of her, and she wished to give him all she could. They dueled, teased, and dipped with their tongues until she was nearly gasping for air.

"Halt!"

She jerked back at the interruption. Torcall leaped to his feet but grabbed her hand to keep her close, a possessive move she liked more than she would have expected.

"Who's there?" he shouted. "Stand out where I can see you."

Hairalt stepped away from a tree and strode directly toward them. "Why would you do this, Riley? Why would you kiss a fool like Torcall when you could be mine?"

He came almost within sword reach. Torcall tugged Riley off the bench and stood in front of her, his big body blocking her from Hairalt's sight.

"Hairalt, you've been banished from Cameron land, as you well know. Be gone. And you'll no' be welcome back on Matheson land, either, after disobeying your chieftain's orders."

"I'll no' leave Riley behind. She's fated to be with me!" He crossed his arms and glared.

Riley nearly screamed with frustration at men who wouldn't listen to women. "I want you to go, Hairalt. I'm no' interested in being with you. In any way! Get off my father's land."

The man's face turned scarlet, and he snarled.

"You're just saying that because he's telling you to. If he weren't here, you'd be in my arms, Riley."

"Nay, I would no'. Leave. Now."

Torcall let go of her hand and stepped forward, drawing his sword. "If you do no' listen to the lady and be gone, you'll no' be able to kiss anyone ever again."

Hairalt cursed but spun on his heel and left. "You have no' seen the last of me!"

Torcall stood alert and on guard until Hairalt was out of sight. Only then did Riley sink back onto the bench.

Torcall sheathed his sword and returned to her, clasping her hands between his. "Are ye well, Riley? You're shaking." He sat close to her and pulled her close. She leaned gratefully into his warmth and comforting strength.

"I wish he would go away and never return."

Somehow, she knew that would never happen. He would be back.

CHAPTER FOURTEEN

WHEN TORCALL WAS sure Riley was well, he followed Hairalt some distance to make sure he would not be lying in wait for them. The fool left a clear trail that led away from Cameron Castle, so Torcall returned to Riley reassured that for now, at least, Hairalt would not bother them again.

As he approached the bench where Riley sat, he saw that the young monk from the abbey had joined her there. He hadn't liked the feel of the man the first time he'd seen him, and he didn't like him any better now. Ruari came alongside him and spotted Bate with Riley.

"That one does no' act like any monk I've ever met," the older man said.

"Surely I can trust a monk, aye?"

Ruari chortled. "I'm not so sure. He's new, and I don't care if he's a monk or no', I would no' want him that close to my lass. They're just as capable of sinning as the rest of us."

Torcall scowled, staring at Ruari. "But in that way? I guess I need to be more alert."

"Much more alert, but 'tis only how I feel

because she's my niece. I treasure her. Do you?"

"Of course I do!" Torcall nearly shouted. "Why do you think I'm still on Cameron land and not on my way home with Shaw? I followed Hairalt to make sure he left and didn't just lurk in the bushes somewhere. 'Twas for her safety, and I did no' like to leave her."

"Good. Stand up to these bastards. Or mayhap I should say the bastard and the monk. You did a fine job with the other one, now move in and get rid of this one."

Torcall moved over to the two seated at the table. They were enjoying the food he'd brought for *their* picnic. He could not fault Riley for sharing with the religious man, but he did wish he hadn't needed to leave her to another man's attentions, even if he was a monk.

Given all that had happened, he thought it best to just return to safety. Perhaps Ruari had a point.

"Hairalt has gone for now, Riley, but I think we should return to the keep." He decided to be factual and hope she'd accept his reasoning. "Hairalt did say he would return, and I do no' trust him. Ruari is headed to the keep as well, and I think we should go with him."

Bate said, "Your safety is most important, my lady, and I didn't like that man at all. I have no sword with me to protect you. You should do as your guard and uncle say."

Torcall breathed a sigh of relief when the monk agreed with him.

"Aye," Riley said. "Hairalt makes my skin crawl, and I've no wish to meet him again, whether my companion has a sword or no. Let's return to the castle, Torcall."

They retrieved their horses, and Torcall helped her mount. He loved placing his hands on her waist and wished he could touch her in other ways. He hoped that someday soon they would take their relationship further. Until then, he enjoyed what they had.

Riley seemed preoccupied, so their conversation was limited on the way back. He watched their surroundings, looking for any sign that Hairalt might have returned. Ruari, too, continually turned his head this way and that, on alert. As Torcall rode, the monk's face invaded his thoughts. He hadn't liked the man, but he couldn't say why. He was just glad Riley had agreed to return to the castle so easily.

The castle courtyard bustled with activity when they rode in. A small celebration was planned for the eve in honor of Connor and Sela's arrival. Torcall vowed to stay close to Riley all evening. He had to protect Riley, because he didn't trust Hairalt not to return. If the bastard got word of the event, he'd come, knowing he could get into the castle unnoticed among the other guests.

Riley slid from her saddle before he could reach her to help her dismount. She shot him a smile.

"I must see Papa and thank him," she said, blushing, then she hurried into the keep.

She would be safe enough inside. He wanted to ride another patrol, just to be sure Hairalt wasn't nearby. He told Ruari his plan and turned his horse for the gate.

He returned to the courtyard hours later, unsure if he was relieved or frustrated that he'd caught no sight of Hairalt.

He took the time to wash and change into fresh clothes before going to the great hall for the evening meal and festivities. Relegated to the guard table while Riley sat at the dais, he had little chance of conversing with her, so he strategized exactly how to be ready for Hairalt's arrival. He memorized every entrance to the hall from the outside, and the quickest way to get from his seat to Riley and then to get her to safety. But the meal passed without incident, and he began to breathe more easily.

After dinner, many of the guards returned to their posts. Torcall made his way toward the hearth. It would give him the best vantage point to see all who came and went. He found himself unable to keep his fingers away from his sheathed sword. He ought not even be wearing it for this occasion, but he knew Aedan and Shaw both would approve his decision. Both wished him to protect Riley.

Every time he looked at the lass, his lass, he thanked the Lord for his good fortune. This eve she wore a dark purple gown with lavender ribbons. Her hair was free, falling in long dark waves over her shoulders.

He had the sudden urge to see her unclothed with her waves falling just as they were now. Then he chastised himself for impure thoughts when she was not far away.

Riley stood in a group with Sela and her

mother, giggling and chatting about something while Connor, Ruari, and Aedan were seated at a trestle table having a serious conversation. A few of the guards were seated with their wives or sweethearts, having a last bite of food or swallow of ale while a minstrel tuned his harp, preparing to entertain those remaining in the hall.

Dyna appeared next to Torcall, seeming to come from out of nowhere. "Stop worrying about him and worry about yourself."

"I have no worries for myself." He took his hand from the hilt of his sword and crossed his arms.

"Aye, you do. Listen to your dreams. You'll regret it if you don't." The lass was comely, her pale blonde hair done up in braids wrapped around her head in the style of the Norse folk. He'd never seen blue eyes quite like hers. They didn't sparkle but had an intensity that unnerved him.

"I didn't have any dreams last eve," he said.

The minstrel began to play, and a pair of guards joined in with a drum and a pipe, the sound covering all the conversations in the great hall.

She snorted. "You dream every night. Everyone does. You must work to recall them. Someone is trying to reach you, and you've shut your mind to that person." She sat in a large chair, turned sideways and flopped her long legs over the arms of the chair. If she were a wee bit older, the position would be uncouth, her gown pulled up closer to her knees that way.

"I have no' shut my mind. What are you talking about?"

She narrowed her eyes at him and declared, "If you do no' wish to hear them, you will no'. You must accept the gift you've been given in order to benefit from it. Stop fighting it."

"What gift?"

"You could be a seer if you would accept it. It could change your life. It could save someone's life, as well."

Torcall had guessed that was what she was about, but how did such a young lass understand the skills of a seer? Or know who was to become one? Too many questions bounced around in his mind. "I like my life the way it is. What would being a seer do to make it better?"

"There's more to be known about Hairalt, for one. All I know is that someone is trying to send you a message, and you need to hear it, or risk disaster." She lunged to her feet and walked away, heading toward her sire. But she stopped and faced him for one last comment. "He's gone for now, but do you not wish to know more of his movements?"

Torcall just stared at her, uncertain what to say or what to think.

He shook his head and looked around. A lass grabbed Brin's hand and brought him to dance in front of the minstrels. A few guards joined them, and Dyna stared at him, then pointed to Riley. That message, at least, was clear enough.

He moved toward Riley and held his hand out to her.

"Will you dance, my lady?"

"With pleasure, kind sir."

She clasped his hand with a wide smile and tugged him out to the group of dancers. They began to move to the music, quick steps that made him feel light on his feet.

The happiness on Riley's face was so beautiful that he couldn't take his eyes from her. She was stunning this eve. Every other lass paled compared to her radiant beauty. No one would guess just from looking at her that she had visions and spoke with the dead.

Had she been chosen to receive her gift, or was it chance? And the ability Dyna seemed so certain he had? What exactly had the girl meant about shutting his mind? He pushed his swirling thoughts away until later. For now, he'd enjoy the dancing.

They danced for nearly an hour before finally pausing for breath. Ruari clapped Torcall on the shoulder and smiled, a clear sign of approval.

Torcall bowed to Riley. "Thank you, my lady."

"It was my pleasure, sir." She winked at him. "Please excuse me for a few moments."

"Of course. When you return, perhaps we can sit and share a pastry and a cup of mead."

He watched her cross to Sela, and the two of them, heads together and smiles on their faces, disappeared down a passageway that led to the ladies' retiring room and the garderobe. He moved over to the hearth and joined a group of men who were talking about the weather signs they'd seen and what they portended for the coming winter. Torcall didn't care—if Riley was in his life, his heart would be warm.

He had thought about escorting her, but she seemed to wish to go alone. He guessed she had to take care of her needs and wished for some privacy. His guess was correct, unfortunately. Fate had thought the same thing because a short time later she entered from the short passageway that held the garderobe, a man's arm snaked around her waist holding her tight. The look of fright on her face nearly ripped his guts out.

The man was dark-haired and bearded, a plaid Torcall didn't recognize wrapped close about his shoulders. Torcall edged closer, not wanting to spook the man as he forced Riley around the edge of the hall toward the outside door.

Only when he was close enough to hear the man's voice did he realize it was Hairalt, disguised beyond recognition.

"Halt!" Torcall had his sword in his hand before he realized it.

Connor Grant was nearly as quick. Unfortunately, neither of them noticed the dagger Hairalt held against the soft skin of Riley's neck until they were nearly upon him.

"Stand back! Unless you'd like to see me slice her neck in front of you. She's mine, and she will die before I give her up. We're leaving and no one will follow us, or you'll never see her alive again."

"Let her go, Hairalt," Torcall said. "This is a strange way to show you care for a lass."

Aedan said, "My guards are already surrounding the castle. You will never get beyond the wall."

"Nay, they'll let me through. She'll marry me and be my wife. 'Tis all your faults that you'd not accept the best husband for her. I tried to do this the right way, but I was rejected. I don't accept rejection. If you knew me at all, you would know this to be true."

Dyna strolled over and stood just to the right of Connor, a child facing down a villain. Torcall whispered, "Get back, lass."

Connor said, "Leave her be."

Dyna smiled at Torcall, then turned her intense gaze on Hairalt. "So let me see if I understand this correctly. You wish us all to believe you love Riley? None of us do. You care only for yourself. Riley, he plans to take you to the fair in Inverness. And then Edinburgh, Glasgow, mayhap London. He may even take you across the Channel to France or farther."

"Close your daft mouth. Who the hell are you? Riley, who is she?" Hairalt twitched nervously.

Riley whispered, "My cousin. She is a seer."

"The hell she is," Hairalt shouted. "You cannot see aught."

Hairalt's hand was shaking. Dyna cast a quick look at her sire, who gave an even more subtle nod. Hairalt, his attention on Riley, didn't seem to notice the silent communication.

Dyna strolled back and forth in front of Hairalt, her pacing annoying but not menacing. "I see a man trying to sell your special talent, Riley. He's planning to make a pile of coin on you, and he'll keep it all for himself. He's going to make you travel as an act and charge people money to see you. He wishes to make coin from your special talents, tell the world that you are an odd creature, call you the woman who can speak with the dead."

"Shut up!" Hairalt shouted. "Shut your lying mouth, you urchin!"

Yet Dyna continued pacing, annoying, scheming. Her tone was sarcastic, brutal. "You must think Riley is a fool, daft, if you thought she could ever agree to go with you."

Hairalt bellowed, "Liar, you lie! You know naught! How could you know!"

"Did you know, Riley, that the fool has already sent a missive to our king to see if he will pay Hairalt for your abilities? The Scottish king first, but the English king if he will pay more to have you answer to him, to speak to all their dead relatives. Their mothers, their fathers, their children."

Riley's tears flowed freely, covering her cheeks as Dyna continued. As if being held at knife-point weren't bad enough, to have Dyna's words hitting her had to be torture.

"Stop," Torcall said to Dyna. "Please. Look what you are doing to her."

<hr>

Riley wished to hug Torcall and never let go. He saw *her*, not Hairalt. He saw her pain and fear and yearned to stop it.

She took in the love and anguish on Torcall's face, the frustration with Dyna's behavior, and she knew that he was the man for her. Their eyes met, and she knew all would be well if he were at her side.

She shifted her gaze to her mother, who was in tears. Then she saw the fury in her father's face, Uncle Ruari's, Brin's.

But not Connor's. Connor stood calm and expressionless, his eyes a cold, steely gray that sparkled with some emotion she couldn't recognize. But then she did.

Pride.

Pride in his daughter.

Dyna sang out, "Come see Riley Cameron! The oddest lass in all the land, the one who can communicate with the dead. She'll speak with your mother, your father, whomever you wish. Just one gold coin and she'll tell all. Angel or demon? You decide!"

Riley saw Torcall move, but Connor stilled him.

Torcall's eyes glistened with unshed tears. For her.

Dyna said, "Or was it ten gold coins? How much did you offer to sell her for?"

Hairalt spat out his answer. "Nay, I only said one silver coin to our king." Then he clamped his mouth shut, realizing he'd just confessed, all because of a child's manipulation.

Riley shivered at the same time she caught a subtle nod from Dyna to her sire.

Dyna stopped with her back to Hairalt and made a motion Riley didn't quite catch, but the lass kept up her verbal assault on her captor.

"Hairalt, you said fifty gold coins to our king!"

"I did no'! I never asked for that. Never said

those words to anyone." Hairalt shoved Riley aside and raced toward Dyna, his dagger aimed at the middle of her back. Someone screamed, but Dyna just stepped calmly aside. Making way for her sire's sword. Connor struck the bastard down before Hairalt even saw him coming.

Connor was the fastest swordsman she'd ever seen, but Torcall was a close second, moving in immediately beside her cousin. But as Hairalt crumpled to the ground in a pool of his own blood, Torcall dropped his sword and rushed for her.

She fell into his warm arms and sobbed.

"Forget all of your wee cousin's words. You are no unnatural creature or strangeling, nor demon nor even angel, and I thank God for it. You're the most beautiful lass ever to live. Do no' believe those cruel words." He wrapped her in his embrace, found a chair, and settled her on his lap, whispering in her ear. "Never. No one thinks that of you."

Torcall didn't think her a freak of nature. That was all that mattered. She held on to him as if she could never let go.

She hated Hairalt, hated all the people who thought she was odd. All those who laughed at her, stared at her, whispered about her abilities.

It wasn't a gift, but sometimes a curse.

It had nearly caused her death.

What would she do now?

CHAPTER FIFTEEN

TORCALL STOOD BY the hearth, drinking gratefully from the tankard in his hand. Riley had gone to bed, her mother close at hand. He'd seen much on Matheson land, from the curse and all that surrounded it, to the revelation of the MacKinnies' scheming, but never anything like that evening's events. The coordination between Connor and Dyna, synchronized so perfectly, happened as if Dyna knew exactly when Hairalt was going to lose control and what he would do when he did.

Dyna came across the hall with a fruit tart in her hand, her father and Aedan behind her.

"I did know exactly when he would lose it," she said, then took a big bite of the treat. Juice trickled down her hand.

"I should have suspected you would know I was thinking that. Do seers' skills run so strong through all the Grant clan?" He shook his head in wonder. He'd only recently become accustomed to Riley's abilities. "What are your skills exactly? Do you have visions like Riley's?"

"Nay. I can sense things like a person's thoughts

or if something important is going to happen. Like the sense I had that my parents and I needed to come here this day." She licked the juice off her fingers with a loud slurp. In some ways, she was older than her years, and in others, exactly the lass she appeared to be.

"Tell me more." He felt as though he was about to enter a new world. Riley had special skills, and according to Dyna Grant, so did he. But he had no idea how to access them.

Dyna chuckled. "You have to open your mind. Listen."

"Listen to what? My dreams?"

"Aye, your dreams. But everything else, too. You have to accept it, then practice it. I practice by moving through a busy hall, keeping my mind open to everything. I can't hear all thoughts, only the thoughts that will be causing immediate action or the most important thoughts. The more dramatic the action, the louder the sound is. It's like a ringing bell goes off in my head when I know that person is about to act. I knew Hairalt was thinking about attacking and letting go of Riley, so I gave the sign to my father."

"I noticed your nods and the sign you made with your hand. That told him what?"

"To get ready to kill the bastard," Connor said. "My daughter's senses have often prevented tragedies, like tonight."

Aedan and Connor took seats by the hearth while Dyna did odd little dances around the nearly empty hall. Hairalt's death had understandably dampened the festive atmosphere, and most people had left soon after.

"Your coordination was amazing to watch, my lord," Torcall said to Connor.

"The important thing is we got him before he got Riley," Connor said.

"If he'd tried to leave this keep, he wouldn't have gotten far, but I favor your method, Grant," Aedan said. "Though it's a good thing your aunt is a healer and knows how to get blood off the floor."

They all chuckled, then Connor said, "We'll be leaving at first light. It seems this eve was the reason Dyna felt such a strong need to be here. Best of luck to you and Riley, Torcall. I'm open for another wedding soon." He looked to Aedan and smiled.

Aedan muttered, "Not quite yet."

Connor swept Dyna into his arms, and they headed up the staircase together.

"My thanks to you, Dyna!" Torcall called as they climbed.

She waved to him. "My work is done here. 'Tis up to you now, Torcall. Open your mind."

If only he knew what she meant.

***

Torcall woke up abruptly, sitting up in bed. He'd had a dream, but he couldn't remember it. Sweat dripped off his brow, and he wiped it away then rested his elbows on his knees and held his head in his hands.

It was nearly Christmas, and he was sweating in

a chamber with only dying embers in the hearth.

He closed his eyes and tried to gather the tendrils of his dream. He'd seen a woman, a beautiful woman who looked a bit like Riley's mother, Jennie. She called to him, as if wanting to tell him something, but he couldn't move. He was frozen to the spot where he stood…outside the keep, he thought.

"You must listen," the dream woman had said.

That was all he recalled.

He ran his hand through his hair, trying to smooth the bird's nest he'd created by tossing in his sleep, then got up to go outside to empty his bladder. He could use the garderobe, but he wanted the clear night air.

He walked out through the small door in the curtain wall, the guards nodding to him as he stepped out, and he waved to them. More than anything, he needed to clear his head.

He found a tree a distance away from the castle and took care of his needs. It was cold, but he didn't care, pacing some before he found broad oak to rest against once he sat. Closing his eyes, he did his best to recall every part of the dream, just as Dyna had told him. If it was his job to protect Riley, he needed to do so.

Moments later, there stood the same woman he'd seen in his dream. She wore a dark green woolen gown, ribbons of gold twined through the bodice. Her hair fell in waves down her back and was a rich, chestnut brown, a shade lighter than Riley's. She wore a beautiful smile, but as she approached him, the smile faded.

"Who are you?" he asked as he pushed himself to his feet, grateful to feel the rough bark of the tree against his back. It anchored him to the knowledge that this was real and not a dream.

"I am someone who loves Riley verra much. I have many beautiful grandchildren, but Riley and Dyna are special, but in different ways. They've been given talents they are just learning how to use. But Riley needs your help. You must listen carefully whenever you are worried about a situation."

"How? Dyna tried to tell me, but I don't understand."

"When someone is about to hurt another, you'll hear an odd tone, and that will serve as a warning. You must work to hear it, but if you practice enough, it will begin to come more easily. Please, Torcall Massie. My dear, sweet Riley needs you."

"I'll do my best." He didn't know what else to say.

"Oh," she said, "And do not worry. She loves you verra much. Don't be afraid to tell her how you feel."

"Please, who are you? What is your name?"

"Tell my daughter that her boots are not sturdy enough."

She turned to leave, but he couldn't let her go. "Wait! Who is your daughter?"

"Torcall, you must learn quickly. Riley will need your skills today or you will lose her."

"What? When? What must I do?"

She smiled again and said, "You'll know. Be alert!"

Someone shook his shoulder hard, and he spun, shrugging whoever it was away. "Leave me be." And he blinked his eyes open to discover he was still sitting against the old oak.

"Massie, wake up. You're having a nightmare. Sounds like you're yelling at the birds." Brin stood in front of him. "You have a chamber inside. Why are you sleeping out here? Do you no' know you'll freeze to death by morn?"

Torcall stood and searched around him, shaking his head to clear it. "The woman. Did you see her?"

"Woman? There was no one here. I could see you from the wall. As soon as I noticed you not moving, I came out. The guards said you'd been out here for an hour or more. Why would you no' return to your chamber?"

Torcall just shook his head. He'd been dreaming, but this time, just like Dyna had told him, he listened. He must have met Riley's grandmother.

Someone was going to try to kill Riley today, and he was the only one who could stop it.

CHAPTER SIXTEEN

RILEY PADDED DOWN the stairs and into the hall. She took a honey cake from the sideboard where breakfast had been laid out and crossed to the hearth, where her mother sat with her needlework.

"Mama, will you please plait my hair?"

"Of course. Bring that stool over to sit on. How do you feel? 'Twas an awful evening. I'm so sorry it happened, but at least you weren't hurt."

She nodded, remembering her terror and confusion when Hairalt grabbed her after she came out of the garderobe. She could still feel the blade of his dagger against her neck. "I'm trying to forget most of it."

"Most of it? Not all?" She pulled the comb through her daughter's long waves, using her fingers to straighten the most tangled areas.

"I want to remember Torcall. Everyone else was paying attention to Hairalt and Dyna, but he saw my fear. I think he does love me." She leaned into her mother's soothing ministrations, her movements skilled and comforting.

"I agree with you. How do you feel about him?"

She tugged on an unusually knotted section, Riley flinching but saying nothing. "Sorry, dear."

She could feel the blush creep up her neck and cross her cheeks. Brin came in from the kitchens with a bowl of apples and held it out in front of her. She took one and cradled it in her hands. "I love him. I do. Has he come in for his morning meal yet?"

"I do no' think you'll see him soon," Brin said.

"Nay? What about Connor and Dyna? I did not have a chance to thank them last eve."

"They left at first light and said to tell you they'll see you soon at the wedding."

"What wedding?" She turned her head the best she could since her mother was still working on her hair.

"Your wedding, sister. Dyna said you and Torcall will marry next."

"But he hasn't even asked Papa for my hand or told me anything of his plans. Mama, do you think she could be right?"

"Dyna does see things that are to come sometimes. You've heard the tales, surely, how she's prevented harm from coming to her other cousins." Her mother tied her plait off. "My brother tells me she is amazing. Alick, Els, and Alasdair get into all kinds of trouble because of her. But she's also saved their lives, just like she did last night for you."

"She has no fear," Brin said. "She's amazing to watch."

"Only because she trusts her father so much," their mother said.

"So where is Torcall?" Riley asked.

Brin gestured in the general direction of the guards' quarters. "He had a sleepless night. I found him sleeping against a tree before dawn. He was having a nightmare, I think. And I bet he had one that sent him outside. He had an odd expression on his face, and he wasn't making sense at first. But I'm sure he'll be fine after he gets some more sleep. I sent him to his bed."

"He was probably dreaming about last night. It was frightful for all of us," their mother said.

Brin took an apple. "Aye. I'm headed outside to speak with Da."

As Brin opened the door, someone stepped inside. "Message for Lady Riley."

Brin sent the messenger, one of the stable lads from the abbey, over to her. "Brother Bart invites you for a meal just before high sun this day. He has made you something special to ease your memories of last eve."

Riley didn't wish to go. She was more interested in speaking with Torcall, but her mother said, "Go ahead and go. The abbey relaxes you."

"I suppose so," Riley said. She turned to the boy. "I'll be there. Please give Brother Bate my thanks for the invitation."

Riley's mother sent the boy out via the kitchen so he could pick up a fruit tart for the walk back to the abbey. Just as he left, Torcall entered the hall.

Her mother smiled. "Good morn, Torcall. Please excuse me—I must go to the kitchens."

Riley, grateful for the privacy, returned her mother's smile.

Then they were alone—both she and Torcall had slept late into the day. In fact, she'd have to ride to the abbey in another hour.

"Good morn to you, Riley. How did you sleep?"

She moved from her stool to a table and motioned for him to sit across from her. "'Twas far from restful, but I believe I slept better than you did. I heard you had nightmares and spent half the night under a tree."

Even with bags under his blue eyes, he was handsome as could be. "Not half the night, but more than was wise, I expect. Have you plans for the day? I was hoping we could go for a ride. It looks to be a sunny day."

"I would love to. And I also must thank you again for all you did for me last night."

"I did naught. It was your cousin and his daughter who did the most."

She reached across for his hand. "But you held me when the tears came. I'll not forget that ever, Torcall. You were wonderful."

"I am simply glad you were not injured. I will hold you any time you need me to." He grinned. "Perhaps you might need to be held after we've ridden a little way from the castle."

Riley bit back a giggle. "I'm helping Mama with a new gown she's making for me, and then I'm going to the abbey around midday."

"Then I will ride with you."

"You need no' go if you are overtired. Brin will

escort me, and Uncle Ruari can return with me."

Torcall got an odd look on his face as if he were answering someone else. It passed quickly, though, and he turned his attention back to her. "'Tis my duty and pleasure to protect you. Shaw ordered me to do so. I will travel with you."

"Fine. I know you will do whatever Shaw told you to do. I look forward to it."

He stood and said, "I promised your brother I would spar with him. He's trying to build his skills to Connor's level." He stood, then gave her a slight bow. "Until our time later."

Her mother came in just then. "Come, lass. I'd like to finish this gown."

Torcall nodded and turned to leave, his broad shoulders nearly filling the doorway. Riley sighed as he left, both happy and uneasy at the same time.

"What's wrong?" her mother asked.

"I'm not sure, but something is bothering him."

Did it have something to do with her? What had been in those nightmares of his?

Torcall was more than restless. He'd dreamt about Riley's grandmother, been warned that she would be in trouble today, yet he had no idea how to help prevent that trouble from happening. How could he begin to know exactly when that trouble would happen? Or what form it would take?

Perhaps a tree was going to fall on her or a bolt of lightning would strike her. And how could he possibly stop those kinds of events from happening?

He'd gone over everything in his mind several times, but with Hairalt gone, he had no idea who or what the threat could be.

He'd investigated every corner of the keep and listened to everyone, been open to angry tones, tone changes, loud tones, any kind of aura around anyone, but he'd heard naught. He'd even listened to silent rooms, hoping he might pick up something that would indicate *where* the threat would come.

What the hell was he supposed to do?

He sparred with Brin until he saw Riley exit the keep and head toward the stables.

"Hellfire, Massie! You can no' just stop and stare at her every time you see her. I nearly put my sword through your thigh," Brin said.

"Sorry. I was just thinking I should go to the abbey with her."

"We'll both escort her, make sure she arrives safely, then give her her privacy. Naught is going to happen to her there." Brin sheathed his sword and hustled toward the stable to help Riley with her horse.

Torcall followed, but instead of fetching his own mount, he made himself look a fool by standing near her and listening. He knew it looked odd, but he was doing what he was told. But he heard nothing, either with his ears or in his mind.

As they rode toward the abbey, he had a sudden idea. He could speak with Riley's mother. Riley's grandmother had given him a message for her—

at least he thought the message must be for her—and perhaps she would have some insight into the rest of the dream.

At the door to the abbey, he squeezed Riley's hand. "I'll give you time for your meditations and return for you in an hour, my lady. Will that suit you?"

"Aye, Torcall. I'll be ready. And you must stop calling me your lady. I'll see you soon." She went inside.

He looked to Brin. "Will you stay, just in case? I've an errand back at the castle, but I'll be quick."

"Aye, Torcall. I've no need to spend my mount riding back and forth."

As Torcall rode back into the castle courtyard, he spotted Jennie speaking with Aedan near the door to the hall. By the time he'd dismounted, Aedan was headed to the guard house, while Jennie waited for him, seeming to know he wished to speak with her.

"My lady, may I have a moment of your time, please?" Torcall asked.

"Of course, Torcall. You look as though you've seen a ghost."

"I may have."

She motioned him to a bench in a small cluster of trees inside the curtain wall. "We can talk privately here. What is bothering you?"

"I had a dream last night." He paused to consider his best approach.

"Brin said you had nightmares. I'm sorry to hear that. It was a trying night for all of us."

"Aye. But I think these were more than simply

dreams. While she was here, Dyna told me I needed to listen to my dreams. I didn't understand what she meant, and I'm still not certain, but last night's dreams were different from any I recall having before, and I'm not sure how to take them. I'm wondering if something I learned would mean anything to you."

"Go ahead. I'll help if I can."

He stared at the ground for a moment and closed his eyes, trying to recall the woman's exact words. "I met a woman in my dreams who said to give her daughter a message. I believe she means you."

"You dreamed about my mother?" Jennie's eyes widened, but she didn't look skeptical at all. If he had to put a word to her expression, he'd say she looked *eager*. "Tell me more. What did she look like?"

"She looked like you. Her hair was down to her waist, the same color as yours. She wore a forest green gown with golden ribbons. She said to tell her daughter—you—that your boots are not sturdy enough."

Jennie jumped up from the bench, her hand going to cover her mouth. Her eyes glistened with moisture, but she took a deep breath and sat down again. "That is something my mother lectured me about all the time. Always telling me my boots were not sturdy enough. Whatever else she told you in the dream, you need to listen to her. What did she say?"

"That Riley would be in danger today, and it was up to me to save her."

Jennie grabbed his hand. "Go to the abbey. Go now! She's having lunch with Bate. Aedan doesn't like him and neither does Ruari. I will be directly behind you. I must get Aedan."

Torcall didn't wait. He mounted his horse and raced back to the abbey. He was sure his horse was galloping through honey, it seemed to take so long.

Brin ran out to him. "What's wrong?"

"Riley. Where is she?"

"Inside. I'll show you the way. Why?"

"I think she's in trouble. I'll explain later."

They entered the abbey and nearly slammed into a nun.

Brin barely slowed as he spoke. "Sister, can you tell me where Riley is? She came in to meet with Bate for lunch."

"I just saw him taking her to the greenhouse. 'Tis the quietest place for visitors and warm in the sun. He said she had a terrible night last eve."

"Many thanks!"

They headed down one of the long passageways and turned a corner to another passageway.

Torcall's head swam. Though the passageway they ran down was empty, he heard a voice, and it sounded contorted, like an echo that had gotten tangled up in itself.

A man said, "Drink this, Riley."

And Torcall knew.

Bate intended to hurt Riley.

CHAPTER SEVENTEEN

RILEY WISHED SHE could have simply come to the abbey with Torcall, strolled the grounds with him at her side, and allowed the previous evening's events to pass into memory. She didn't want to share a meal with Bate, but she'd agreed to come. Her only hope was to get it over with quickly and find Torcall. But Bate was acting strangely.

"My, but you are lovely today, Riley." He spent too much time fussing over what he'd prepared for lunch. He paced back and forth, going back to the wine bottle three times, but never pouring it.

What was going on in his mind?

"Did I tell you how lovely you look today, Riley?" he asked with a nervous chuckle.

"Aye, you have. What's wrong, Bate?" Something was off about him, but she didn't know what.

They were in the greenhouse where he'd set a tablecloth on a small table with two chairs, a light meal on the table. There was a bottle of wine on the shelf behind him, a fresh loaf of bread, well-aged cheese, thin slices of cold roast beef, and a pastry made with pears.

She loved pears.

But she didn't like being alone with Bate, and if she'd known their meal was to be like this, she wouldn't have come. This felt intimate.

He poured her some wine and said, "Here, try it and see if you like it."

"Nay, not yet. I'd rather have something to eat first."

"Please drink it. I chose it especially for you."

She sighed and accepted the goblet, took a sniff to see if the aroma was pleasing. She could tell whether she would like a wine just by its scent. This one had an odd aroma to it. She scowled.

"Have you tried it? It smells different." She set the goblet back down, not anxious to taste it yet. Perhaps it was one of those wines that needed to rest before it acquired its peak flavor.

"Aye, it's quite pleasing. Please drink it. You'll love it."

How would he know what wine would appeal to her? If she took a sip, perhaps he would stop pestering her about it. She brought the goblet to her lips, but before the wine touched her mouth, the door burst open. Her brother barged in with Torcall directly behind him.

Torcall rushed to her side. "Nay! Do not drink it!"

"Torcall, what is wrong with you? 'Tis just a glass of wine."

"Please, Riley. The wine is wrong, not I."

She set the goblet down. Torcall had never led

her wrong. She trusted him without hesitation. Her mother said he loved her, and he would do nothing that would harm her.

"If you say the wine is bad, I won't drink it. But, Torcall, how do you know? What is this about?"

Bate grabbed the goblet and thrust it against her lips, rough and insistent. "Drink. It. Now."

"Nay." Torcall grabbed the goblet and took a sip, then wrinkled his nose in distaste. "I was right. This wine is no good." He poured it into the soil in a nearby planter.

"Stop, it is not for you!" Bate leaped for Torcall and knocked the cup out of his hand, but by then it was empty.

Riley backed up at the crazed look in Bart's eyes. They reminded her of Hairalt's eyes last eve. What in the world was happening? As if Bate, Brin, and Torcall weren't enough, her parents burst into the greenhouse as well.

Shouts filled the greenhouse. Bate ran across the room, heading toward the back door, and her father bellowed, "Brin, get him! Do no' allow him to leave!"

Brin and her father chased Bate while her mother stepped out the main door and yelled, "Help! I need some help back here!"

Torcall calmly set the empty cup on the table and gathered Riley into his arms. "Torcall, what in the world is going on?" She cupped his cheek. "Did ye drink the wine or no'?"

"Only the smallest sip," he said, his lips moving against her hair. He took a deep breath and let it out slowly. "Only enough to taste the poison. But I think 'tis making me a wee bit sleepy."

Her mother joined them, wrapping her arms around both Riley and Torcall where they stood. "The daft monk tried to poison you, Riley. Oh, Torcall, you are nearly as daft as the monk. What were you thinking, taking a drink like that?"

"I had to prove he'd poisoned it. Forgive me, my lady," he said as he dropped into the nearest chair, grabbing the table to steady himself.

Several monks and nuns arrived at that moment, crowding around them.

"My lady, what has happened?" someone asked.

Her mother turned to the group behind her.

"Brother Bate tried to poison Riley. This man"—she shot Torcall a fond look—"drank a wee bit of it. What kind of poisons might he have access to? Please tell me in case he drank enough to be harmed by it. I can prepare a remedy."

The nuns all stared at each other, shaking their heads, but then a monk stepped forward. Riley recognized the abbey's apothecary. "He asked me for a sleeping draught. He said he couldn't sleep and wanted enough for a couple of nights."

"How much did you give him? Enough to kill someone?" Jennie asked, doing her best to calm her voice.

"Nay, just two doses. He wanted enough for three nights, but I wouldn't give him so much." The monk looked at Torcall. "You'll suffer no ill effects from a small sip, sir, even if you drank it at full strength. But you may sleep a bit."

Torcall smiled. "Thank you, Brother. Even if I

had the complete double dose, 'twould be a fair price to pay to keep Riley safe. I just hope the man is caught."

"I'm sorry your day has been so disrupted," Riley said.

The smallest monk laughed. "Most of us love a good disruption every now and then, my lady." He sobered. "But we're the ones who owe you an apology. You were in our care, and your life was endangered. That is a serious sin indeed. We'll do whatever we can to make things right."

Brin came in the back entrance pushing Bate in front of him. Bate's hands were tied behind his back, and he had a smudge of dirt on his not-really-so-handsome-after-all face. Her sire followed them.

"Why, Bate?" Riley asked. "Why would you try to poison me?"

Bate straightened and tried to look defiant. "I didn't try to poison you. Someone else must have put the sleeping draught in the wine."

The man spun one lie after another, the falsehoods chasing each other off his tongue as quickly as a squirrel after a nut.

Torcall stepped forward. "You planned to put her to sleep, place her in that large trunk over there, then smuggle her aboard your ship to Europe. You were hoping her special talents would get you in to meet the Pope."

Bate scowled but seemed to have realized silence was his safest choice.

"How did you figure that out, Torcall?" Riley asked.

He grinned and shrugged. "I finally learned to listen, as well as look. Bate has an awful tone. It was quite grating." He rubbed one ear and tipped his head. "When I saw the trunk in the greenhouse, I thought it odd, and then I saw the holes punched into it, to allow for air to get in. It was like cathedral bells in my head when I put it all together."

"You learned to accept your gift? Dyna told me she spoke to you about it." She was so excited that he had special talents too, she wished to ask him to marry her. Heaven above must have had a hand in bringing together a husband and wife so perfectly matched.

"I have accepted that I have much to learn, but you are my true gift. Will you marry me, Riley? I hear we have many bairns to look forward to."

EPILOGUE

A fortnight later on Black Isle

RILEY MASSIE STOOD in the middle of the faerie glen, hoping Violet would appear. She held her hand out to her husband and he stepped quietly up next to her, gripping her hand more tightly than she'd expected.

"It will be fine, Torcall. I just want her to know that we are together and happy. We won't stay long. I wanted to come here first, get this settled."

He leaned over and kissed her cheek. "I trust you completely, love. But if she wishes for me to leave, I will."

She squeezed his hand and then turned toward the waterfall, hoping Violet was still able to appear before her.

"Violet? I brought someone to see you." Nothing. "Violet, I wanted to make sure you will be able to move on. Did we do enough to help you stay with Nils?"

She heard a rustling in the distance and gave Torcall a tiny nod to let him know Violet was coming.

The trees to the side of the waterfall parted and Violet stepped out in a haze, dressed in a long golden gown, coming to the border to stand in front of them. She appeared to walk across the water without getting wet. Surely something a mere person could not do. "Greetings to you, Riley. Torcall cannot see me yet, but I will allow him to in a moment. I need to say something to you first."

Riley looked at Torcall. "She's here." Her eyes misted as she turned back to the lovely woman in front of her.

Violet said, "You and Torcall were meant for each other. The heavens say so, and you need to know that. Torcall never truly loved me. We were young and didn't know much about love then. I didn't know how to send him away without hurting his feelings." She paused, staring at the ground. A tear fell—Riley hadn't known ghosts could weep. She couldn't stop her own eyes from misting.

Violet raised her head and went on. "I know better now, and I'm sorry I nearly had a part in you two not discovering your love for each other. But I'm so pleased to see you married and happy!" She waved her hands over her head, summoning a thick haze that hid her from sight.

"Violet? Please don't go yet."

"Is there something wrong?" Torcall whispered. In a louder voice, he called, "I didn't mean to hurt you, Violet."

A handful of butterflies flew out of the trees,

and Violet stepped out of the haze. "Greetings, Torcall. You did not hurt me."

Torcall gasped and gripped Riley's hand so hard that she had to pinch him to get him to let go. "I'm sorry," he whispered. "I just can't believe she's actually standing in front of me. Violet, I'm sorry."

"You have naught to apologize for, my dear friend," Violet said. "I'm here to apologize to you. I was in love with Nils, but I was naïve and liked your attention. And I didn't know how to tell you about Nils. And please do not feel sorry for me." She glanced back over her shoulder and held her hand out. A man stepped forward and took it.

"Do you know him?" Riley asked Torcall.

"I do. Greetings, Nils. I'm sorry you both fell victim to the curse."

"Massie, nice to see you again. No need to be sorry. 'Tis most wonderful here, and our love will go on forever. You'll see someday, but not for a long time yet."

Violet blew Riley a kiss and said, "Many thanks for helping me move on. You two will have a wonderful life together, and you'll be blessed with beautiful bairns. But you have work to do yet. You were brought together because you both have special talents, and together, you can accomplish more than you could ever guess."

Riley glanced up at Torcall. By the time she looked back to the other couple, they had disappeared.

Violet's last words floated to them from the dispersing fog. "It's written in the stars."

Torcall engulfed Riley in a deep hug. "Thank you, Riley. I love you so much."

"I love you too."

"Do you think 'tis true? We'll do some important things together?"

"Aye, I always believe what ghosts tell me."

He stepped back and cupped her face. "Truly?"

"It's written in the stars, Torcall."

They left the glen quietly, both in a bit of a daze from all they had just seen. Torcall lifted Riley onto his horse and climbed up behind her.

"I'm glad you are riding with me for this trip."

They didn't rush back, lingering in the forest until dusk, but once they neared the walls of Eddirdale Castle, Riley began to wonder if they should have ridden more quickly.

"What the hell is happening?" Torcall asked.

Chaos reigned, riders and horses filling the courtyard, blue plaids and flickering torches everywhere.

They got as close as they could before dismounting. She peered through the deepening dark and asked, "Uncle Logan? Is it truly you causing all this trouble?"

"Aye, and you had better make way. We were halfway home from your wedding when we received the message that Brigid is delivering. You better get out of Gwynie's way, or she'll knock you down."

A voice behind him barked out, "Oh Logan, close your mouth and get my things. Greetings, Riley. We can chat soon, but we have more important things to see to first."

The two ran by them. Sorcha and Cailean followed, Sorcha shrugging. "Sorry, Riley, but it happens every time a new grandbairn comes along." She rolled her eyes as only Sorcha could, then giggled and waved as they hurried to the keep.

Riley and Torcall followed and finally made it inside only to find Padraig waving them over to the hearth. "You'd better get out of the way. Gisella is running around and doesn't know what to do next, but she's so excited for her two brothers. Where's your mother?"

"A wee bit behind us. Why? Isn't Aunt Brenna here already? She said she was coming here from the wedding."

"She did, but we all had a surprise, and another with midwifery skills would be welcome. Jennet and Brigid are both ready to deliver."

"This eve?"

Padraig nodded.

"I better go back and hurry my mother along."

Her mother, Tara, and Shaw came through the gates just as Riley stepped outside. That meant all the Mathesons were here. "Hurry, Mama. Aunt Brenna needs you. There are two bairns on their way tonight!"

Torcall and Riley followed everyone inside, and the two settled at a trestle table with Tara and Shaw. "Settle in, everyone," Tara said. "If this is anything like the time this happened to Alex Grant, it could last all night."

The chaos continued, and before long, Uncle Quade and Uncle Logan were both pacing the great hall, waiting on word from their wives, who were both upstairs. Marcas paced the balcony, stepping inside the chamber every once in a while to check on Brigid. Ethan said he would not leave Jennet's side.

Logan cursed. "Matheson gets to go inside. Why? Just because he's the chief of the clan?"

Quade drawled, "Mayhap because it's his wife? I have no desire to be inside. I don't wish to see my lassie in pain."

"A father should have rights ahead of the husband," Logan announced. "How many daughters do we have up there, Quade, and not a one can come out and update us on our babies."

A high-pitched wail came from one of the chambers abovestairs. Riley looked at Tara and whispered, "That sounded like Brigid. I hope she's all right."

Tara said, "I'm sure she's fine. You know how childbirth goes."

Riley stared at her uncle Logan, who was staring at the chamber above wide-eyed. "Uncle Logan knows how it goes at this point in his life, but I'm no' sure he remembers by the look on his face." The entire hall quieted, listening to Brigid's wails. Marcas had rushed inside the chamber at the first wail.

Uncle Logan spun around and said, "Matheson, where the hell are you so I can cut your bollocks off for making my wee lassie go through such pain?"

The door to the keep opened and Micheil and Diana came in. "Did we make it in time?"

"Who's that?" Torcall whispered.

"Logan and Quade's brother Micheil and his wife. Diana is chieftain of the Drummonds."

"A female chieftain?" Shaw whistled.

"Where the hell is Lina, Micheil? You know I wanted her here." Logan yelled as he paced.

"She's right behind me, got caught talking. I couldn't wait. I didn't want to miss one moment of you two in your troubles." The large man moved over and clasped the shoulders of his two brothers. "This is fabulous. I think we're in for a great show tonight, Diana."

Diana shook her head, grinned, and climbed the staircase.

Torcall whispered, "Your uncle Logan is the shortest of the brothers but he's the best swordsman?"

"Aye, and best archer, spy, and anything else there is."

Logan barked out, "The best grandsire. 'Tis the most important."

"And the best sense of hearing," Riley said with a laugh.

About half an hour later, Riley's mother came out of one chamber and shouted down from the balcony, "'Tis a lassie, and she's lovely!"

Aunt Brenna flew out of another chamber and stood at the balcony. "A beautiful lassie, Quade. She looks just like Jennet. Not a speck of hair on her head, just like her mother." She clasped her hands together, then turned as if she just noticed her sister standing there. "Jennie?"

Her mother smiled. "A lassie."

"How long ago?"

"A moment only?"

"Truly? It happened again?" The two sisters stood and stared at each other as the rest of the hall hung on their every word. The healers had experienced nearly the same with their brother Alex's grandbabies. They'd delivered three bairns at the same time on a cold night in winter.

"I don't believe it!" Jennie said as she hugged her sister.

"And both are hale?" someone called up from the gathered crowd in the hall.

"Aye, hale and beautiful," Aunt Brenna cried.

The door opened and Avelina strolled in, ignoring everyone as she hiked up the staircase. Aunt Brenna dragged her into Jennet's chamber.

Uncle Logan fell to his knees with glee and bellowed the Ramsay war whoop loudly enough to make everyone cover their ears.

Two lasses, same day, same time.

"Two Ramsay warriors!" Logan whooped again, and Riley laughed at his excitement.

Avelina came out of one chamber, went into the other, then strolled down the staircase, a babe in each arm. Quade, Logan, and Micheil rushed to the bottom of the staircase.

Avelina said, "Not just two Ramsay warriors, but two warrior princesses have been born this day, and I cannot wait to watch them grow into the strong lasses they are meant to be."

All three big burly men leaned forward and cooed at the newly born lassies.

"Brothers, meet Reyna and Isla."

THE END

DEAR READER,
Thanks for reading!

As you can see, this leads directly into my next series. Just as the Highland Swords was the third generation of the Grants with Alasdair, Alick, Els, and Dyna, this next series will be the third generation of the Ramsays along with a few others. But it will begin with Reyna and Isla, celebrating mostly the skills of the Ramsay archers.

Now I just have to come up with a series name. Highland Archers? Highland Bows? We'll see!

I'm hoping to make it a six-book series, but who knows?

Happy reading and happy holidays!

Keira Montclair
www.keiramontclair.com

NOVELS BY KEIRA MONTCLAIR

THE SOULMATE CHRONICLES TRILOGY
#1 TRUSTING A HIGHLANDER
#2 TRUSTING A SCOT
#3 TRUSTING A CHIEFTAIN

STAND-ALONE BOOKS
THE BANISHED HIGHLANDER
REFORMING THE DUKE-REGENCY
WOLF AND THE WILD SCOTS
FALLING FOR THE CHIEFTAIN-3RD in a collaborative trilogy
HIGHLAND SECRETS -3rd in a collaborative trilogy

THE SUMMERHILL SERIES-CONTEMPORARY ROMANCE
#1-ONE SUMMERHILL DAY
#2-A FRESH START FOR TWO
#3-THREE REASONS TO LOVE

ABOUT THE AUTHOR

Keira Montclair is the pen name of an author who lives in South Carolina with her husband. She loves to write fast-paced, emotional romance, especially with children as secondary characters.

When she's not writing, she loves to spend time with her grandchildren. She's worked as a high school math teacher, a registered nurse, and an office manager. She loves ballet, mathematics, puzzles, learning anything new, and creating new characters for her readers to fall in love with.

She writes historical romantic suspense. Her best-selling series is a family saga that follows two medieval Scottish clans through four generations and now numbers over thirty books.

Contact her through her website:
www.keiramontclair.com

Printed in Great Britain
by Amazon

38500091R00089